PIPE FITTINGS

 NIPPLES

 PIPE LENGTHS UP TO 22 FT.

STRAIGHT COUPLING

REDUCING COUPLING

 COUPLING

NUT

 CAP

STRAIGHT TEE

REDUCING TEE

STREET TEE

STRAIGHT CROSS

REDUCING CROSS

 90° ELBOW

 90° ELBOW

90° ELBOW

45° ELBOW

REDUCING ELBOW

90° STREET ELBOW

45° STREET ELBOW

45° Y-BEND

 REDUCING TEE

 REDUCER

UNION (3 PARTS)

PLUG

BUSHING

CAP

RETURN BEND

90°

45°

UNION ELBOWS

STREET

UNION TEES

 PLUG

 45° ELBOW

 TEE

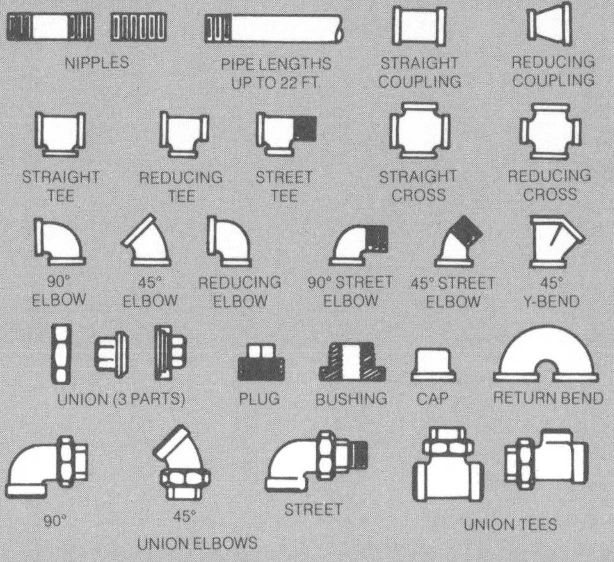

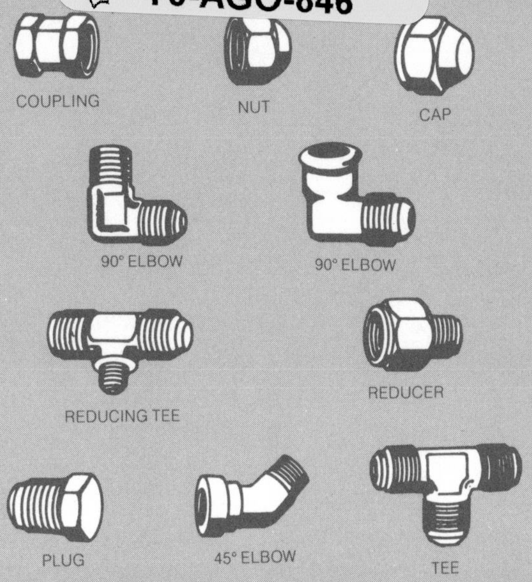

MEASURES OF CAPACITY

1 cup	=	8 fl oz
2 cups	=	1 pint
2 pints	=	1 quart
4 quarts	=	1 gallon
2 gallons	=	1 peck
4 pecks	=	1 bushel

STANDARD STEEL PIPE ((All Dimensions in inches)

Nominal Size	Outside Diameter	Inside Diameter	Nominal Size	Outside Diameter	Inside Diameter
⅛	0.405	0.269	1	1.315	1.049
¼	0.540	0.364	1¼	1.660	1.380
⅜	0.675	0.493	1½	1.900	1.610
½	0.840	0.622	2	2.375	2.067
¾	1.050	0.824	2½	2.875	2.469

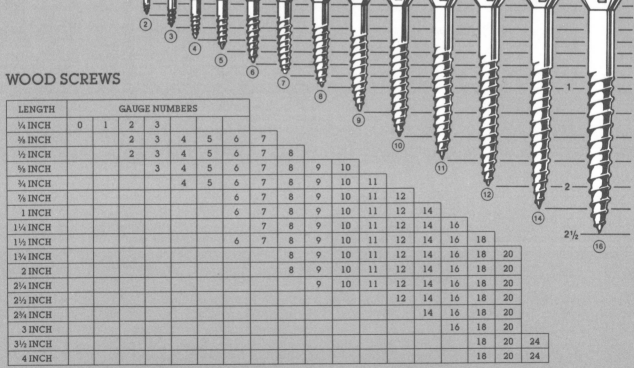

WOOD SCREWS

LENGTH	GAUGE NUMBERS																	
¼ INCH	0	1	2	3														
⅜ INCH			2	3	4	5	6	7										
½ INCH			2	3	4	5	6	7	8									
⅝ INCH				3	4	5	6	7	8	9	10							
¾ INCH					4	5	6	7	8	9	10	11						
⅞ INCH							6	7	8	9	10	11	12					
1 INCH							6	7	8	9	10	11	12	14				
1¼ INCH								7	8	9	10	11	12	14	16			
1½ INCH							6	7	8	9	10	11	12	14	16	18		
1¾ INCH									8	9	10	11	12	14	16	18	20	
2 INCH									8	9	10	11	12	14	16	18	20	
2¼ INCH										9	10	11	12	14	16	18	20	
2½ INCH													12	14	16	18	20	
2¾ INCH														14	16	18	20	
3 INCH															16	18	20	
3½ INCH																18	20	24
4 INCH																18	20	24

WHEN YOU BUY SCREWS, SPECIFY (1) LENGTH, (2) GAUGE NUMBER, (3) TYPE OF HEAD—FLAT, ROUND, OR OVAL, (4) MATERIAL—STEEL, BRASS, BRONZE, ETC., (5) FINISH—BRIGHT, STEEL BLUED, CADMIUM, NICKEL, OR CHROMIUM PLATED.

Popular Mechanics

do-it-yourself encyclopedia

The complete, illustrated home reference guide from the world's most authoritative source for today's how-to-do-it information.

Volume 20

RADIAL-ARM SAWS
to
SABRE SAWS

HEARST DIRECT BOOKS

NEW YORK

Acknowledgements

The Popular Mechanics Encyclopedia is published with the consent and cooperation of POPULAR MECHANICS Magazine.

For POPULAR MECHANICS Magazine:

Editor-in-Chief: *Joe Oldham*

Managing Editor: *Bill Hartford*

Special Features Editor: *Sheldon M. Gallager*

Automotive Editor: *Wade A. Hoyt, SAE*

Home and Shop Editor: *Steve Willson*

Electronics Editor: *Stephen A. Booth*

Boating, Outdoors and Travel Editor: *Timothy H. Cole*

Science Editor: *Dennis Eskow*

Popular Mechanics Encyclopedia

Project Director: *Boyd Griffin*

Manufacturing: *Ron Schoenfeld*

Assistant Editors: *Cynthia W. Lockhart Peter McCann, Rosanna Petruccio*

Production Coordinator: *Peter McCann*

The staff of Popular Mechanics Encyclopedia is grateful to the following individuals and organizations:

Editor: *C. Edward Cavert*

Editor Emeritus: *Clifford B. Hicks*

Production: *Layla Productions*

Production Director: *Lori Stein*

Book Design: *The Bentwood Studio*

Art Director: *Jos. Trautwein*

Design Consultant: *Suzanne Bennett & Associates*

Illustrations: *AP Graphics, Evelyne Johnson Associates, Popular Mechanics Magazine, Vantage Art.*

Contributing Writers: C.E. Banister, *Table for a radial-arm saw*, page 2447; *Molding head fence for a radial saw*, page 2452; James L. Bennett, *Tent trailer you can build*, page 2475; Walter E. Burton, *Shaper from your router*, page 2545; *Table saw from your sabre saw*, page 2555; Rosario Capotosto, *Sabre saw techniques*, page 2551; John E. Gaynor, *Handrail to enhance your home*, page 2458; E.P. Haddon, *Camping expert fits out an RV*, page 2461; R.S. Hedin, *Table extensions for a radial saw*, page 2456; Larry Kellam, *Bench with lots of storage*, page 2453; W. Clyde Lammey, *Radial-arm saw techniques*, page 2436; Wayne C. Leckey, *Reroof with wood shakes and shingles*, page 2515; Bill McKeown, *Vacation home begins with RV*, page 2464; V. Lee Oertle, *Winterize your camper*, page 2467; *Improve your recreational vehicle*, page 2471; Charles R. Self, *Remodeling*, page 2479; William Waggoner, *Jacks quickly level a radial-saw table*, page 2457.

Picture Credits: Popular Mechanics Encyclopedia is grateful to the following for permission to reprint their photographs: Charles Self, page 2479 and 2480.

ISBN 0-87851-173-3

Library of Congress 85-81760

10 9 8 7 6 5 4

PRINTED IN THE UNITED STATES OF AMERICA

Although every effort has been made to ensure the accuracy and completeness of the information in this book, Hearst Direct Books makes no guarantees, stated or implied, nor will they be liable in the event of misinterpretation or human error made by the reader, or for any typographical errors that may appear. WORK SAFELY WITH HAND TOOLS. WEAR SAFETY GOGGLES. READ MANUFACTURER'S INSTRUCTIONS AND WARNINGS FOR ALL PRODUCTS.

Contents

VOLUME 20 • RA to SA

RADIAL-ARM SAWS
Radial-arm saw techniques 2436
Cabinet for your radial-arm saw 2443
Table for a radial-arm saw 2447
Molding head fence for a radial saw 2452
Bench with lots of storage 2453
Table extensions for a radial saw 2456
Jacks quickly level a radial-saw table 2457
See also Bandsaws .... Vol. 2
See also Bench Saws .... Vol. 3
See also Circular Saws .... Vol. 6

RADIATORS
See Cooling Systems, Auto .... Vol. 6

RAILINGS
Handrail to enhance your home 2458
Wrought-iron railing installation 2459
See also Decks .... Vol. 7

RECORD PLAYERS
See Stereo Systems .... Vol. 22

RECORDERS
See Cassette Recorders .... Vol. 5
See TV and Video .... Vol. 23

RECREATIONAL VEHICLES
Camping expert fits out an RV 2461
Vacation home begins with an RV 2464
Winterize your camper 2467
Improve your recreational vehicle 2471
Tent trailer you can build 2475
See also Campers .... Vol. 5
See also Weekend Safety Tips .... Vol. 25

REFINISHING
See Finishing .... Vol. 10
See Painting Tools .... Vol. 17

REFRIGERATORS
See Appliance Repair .... Vol. 1

REMODELING
Remodeling 2479
Remodeling ideas 2481
New Home—without moving 2489
Facelifting—cheapest way to get
    a new home 2492
Dramatic changes you can
    make yourself 2496
Sliding doors and windows
    you can add 2501
Removing a bearing wall 2505
See also Basement Remodeling .... Vol. 2

See also Drywall .... Vol. 8
See also Electrical Wiring .... Vol. 8
See also Entryways .... Vol. 9
See also Family Rooms .... Vol. 9
See also Fireplaces .... Vol. 10
See also Floors and Flooring .... Vol. 10
See also Garages .... Vol. 11
See also Greenhouses .... Vol. 11
See also Home Additions .... Vol. 13
See also Kitchen Projects .... Vol. 14
See also Painting .... Vol. 17
See also Plumbing .... Vol. 19
See also Stairs .... Vol. 22

RETAINING WALLS
See Yard and Garden Projects .... Vol. 27

REUPHOLSTERING
See Upholstering .... Vol. 25

RIFLES
See Guns .... Vol. 11
See Marksmanship .... Vol. 15

ROCK POLISHING
See Hobbies .... Vol. 12

ROOFS
Roofing yourself can save half the cost ... 2509
Damaged roof repair 2513
Reroof with wood shakes and shingles ... 2515
See also Angles .... Vol. 1
See also Carpentry .... Vol. 5
See also Measurements .... Vol. 16

ROOM DIVIDERS
Walls that serve a purpose 2520
Freestanding wall lets you
    divide and conquer 2523
Light a freestanding wall 2526
See also Cabinets .... Vol. 4

ROUTERS
Router techniques 2527
Craftsman's secrets for using a router 2539
Shaper from your router 2545

SABRE SAWS
Sabre saw techniques 2551
Table saw from your sabre saw 2555

SAILBOATS
See Boats and Boating .... Vol. 3

SANDBOXES
See Playgrounds .... Vol. 18

INDEX 2559

Radial-arm saw techniques

■ A RADIAL SAW is comparable to a table saw turned upside down. The motor, arbor, controls and mountings are all *above* the table rather than *below* it.

In crosscutting and mitering operations, and also in dadoing, you move the blade or cutter to the work, rather than the work to the blade or cutter as with the table saw. The exceptions are ripping, and some operations with accessories where the work is moved to the cutter, as in grooving, rabbeting, routing and shaping.

This "upside down" saw calls for a somewhat different operating technique and an extra measure of caution in all operations. This applies even when the blade housing and guard are in position. You will notice when making that first crosscut with your new saw that the blade tends to move, or "pull," toward you as the cut progresses. You are making what experienced operators of radial saws call a "climb" cut, where the blade tends to pull itself into the work. Here you make sure of that extra measure of caution and have a firm hold on the handle with which you draw the blade forward into the workpiece; you actually offer a slight resistance to the travel of the blade into the workpiece. Otherwise the cut may be too fast for smoothness, and the blade may exit from the cut unexpectedly, possibly endangering you. This is especially true when crosscutting or mitering wide pieces of stock 2 in. or more in thickness.

The rules for safe operation of the radial saw are quite simple and should quickly become habit: (a) Before you plug in the tool, make sure the motor switch is in the "off" position. (b) Make sure before starting the motor that all con-trol handles are tightened properly. (c) Never—repeat, *never*—permit loose pieces of stock, other objects such as end cuttings, wrenches, clamps, etc., on the table when operating the unit. (d) Never—repeat, *never*—allow your attention to wander even for a moment while the unit is in operation. (e) Always operate the unit with both the blade housing and the blade guard in position.

All the precautions can be summed up in two words—*be careful!*

The manual that comes with the saw will tell: how to set it up and operate it when making the basic cuts; how to align the blade should this be necessary; and how to arrange the table spacer boards for in and out ripping.

Some radials may come with the table already grooved and recessed. If not you can easily cut these yourself. To make the crosscut groove, raise the blade to clear, slide the carriage back as far as it will go, start the motor, and lower the blade until it cuts into the table about $3/16$ in. Then pull the blade forward as far as it will go. Cut the right and left miter grooves in the same manner, moving the arm 45 degrees to the right and left. Then raise the blade to clear, swing the arm to the 90 degree position, swing the yoke 90 degrees to the out-rip position, pull it forward as far as it will go, start the motor and lower the blade until it cuts into the table about $3/16$ in. Push it back as far as it will go, very slowly, so that it cuts a concave recess in the tabletop. The purpose of the grooves and recess, of course, is to permit the lowering of the blade below the table surface so that it will cut all the way through the stock.

CROSSCUTTING is a basic operation on radial saw. Blade is drawn only far enough to cut through material, then returned to starting position.

WHEN SETTING up for ripping, tilt blade housing to just clear the stock, then adjust kickback arm with a block the thickness of stock to be ripped.

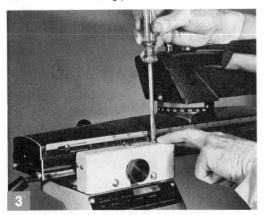

IF YOU HAVE NOT already done so, set rip-scale pointers for in and out-rip positions to assure accuracy. See instructions that come with your saw.

USE PUSH STICK when ripping short, narrow stock. Place stick near outer corner of stock to prevent it drifting away from the fence.

In making the crosscut, Fig. 1, you have a choice of left or right-hand pull. In the illustration, the left-hand pull is shown, as the longer stock is more conveniently held in the position by the right hand. If the workpiece were short, and only a small waste piece was to be removed, you could use the right-hand pull with left-hand hold. Either position is permissible, but you should know where that right or left holding hand is at all times!

When making the crosscut or the miter (either right or left-hand) don't pull the blade all the way past the stock. Stop when the waste is completely severed. This assures that when you move the blade back through the cut, there is no chance that the portion of the blade coming up will catch the waste. The same is true when making the miter cuts.

Before you make a rip cut, always set the anti-kickback arm as in Fig. 2. First tilt the blade guard so that its rear edge will be about ⅛ to ¼

in. above the surface of the stock. Then, if ¾-in. stock is to be ripped, set the kickback arm with the swiveling points, or fingers, in the position shown, using a ¾-in. block. Next, if you have not already done so, set the pointers on the rip scale to the correct positions to assure ripping to the precise width desired, Fig. 3. (See your instruction manual.) In any ripping operation make sure *both yoke and carriage* are locked in position before starting the motor.

When ripping short, narrow stock as in Fig. 4, use a push stick and place the stick so that it contacts the material near the outer edge as shown. This will prevent any tendency of the workpiece to edge away from the fence. Fig. 5 shows the common procedure of ripping a long, wide workpiece. *Here the blade guard has been removed, as it has in other following illustrations, only for the sake of clarity.*

Figs. 6 and 7 show positions in cutting left and right-hand miters. The left-hand miter is the least

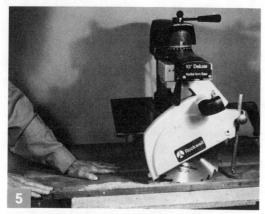

RIP CUT in relatively wide stock is common radial-saw operation. In rip cuts make sure carriage, yoke and blade housing are securely locked in place.

LEFT-HAND miter cut is perhaps less common of the two. As in all crosscutting, draw blade only far enough to cut through stock.

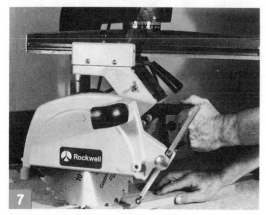

RIGHT-HAND MITER is made just opposite. After first cut, turn stock over and move to left to miter opposite end. Exception is mitering molded stock.

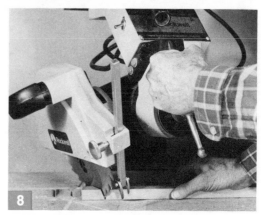

COMPOUND MITER is made by swinging the arm and tilting the blade the required number of degrees. Consult a table for proper degree setting.

used as it generally is possible to shift the stock from right to left positions after turning it over when necessary to miter both ends. The exception, of course, is mitering picture molding. The compound miter, Fig. 8, requires setting both the arm and the tilt to the required number of degrees to form the "hopper" joint. There are tables available which give the degree settings for this type of joinery on the radial-arm saw.

When you want to trim a number of small workpieces to exact length, you can clamp a stop to the fence as in Fig. 9. Make sure that the clamp is properly positioned and that it is *tight*. Remove each waste piece as it is cut only after the saw is moved back to its extreme rear position.

Your radial saw is a first-rate disc sander. You first remove the fence and substitute two ¾-in. square strips, placing these on each side of the disc as in Fig. 10. Then lower the disc through the slot thus formed as in Fig. 11. Be sure that

the disc clears before starting the motor; also be sure that it just clears the fixed edge of the saw table. Use a medium to coarse grade abrasive disc for fast cutting and to avoid burning the end grain of hardwoods. Use the finer grades for finishing, and apply only light pressure to the work.

To use a drum sander, swivel the motor to the vertical position with the spindle, or arbor, down. Cut a half-round opening in the edge of each of the spacer boards, as in Fig. 12. The diameter of the opening should be about 1½ times the diameter of the drum. Leave the square spacers in position as shown in Fig. 11, but be sure that the table clamps are drawn tight so nothing can shift while sanding is being done. Be especially careful to avoid a finger or hand contacting the rotating drum; a rather painful burn can be the penalty. The same caution is necessary when using the disc. Also, in any of these operations, make sure that the yoke is

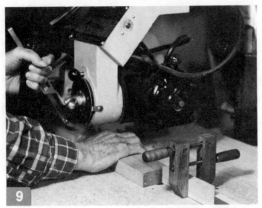

TO CUT DUPLICATE short lengths, clamp a stop to the fence and measure distance from blade to stop. Make sure that the clamp is drawn tight!

FOR DISC SANDING substitute ¾-in. strips for fence, one on each side of disc. Lower disc into opening and be sure carriage and yoke are locked.

WHEN SANDING end grain, use coarse abrasive and a light pressure to avoid "burning" stock. Don't permit hand or fingers to touch the rotating disc.

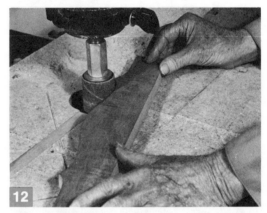

YOUR RADIAL SAW is also a drum sander. Swing motor to vertical position and cut half-round opening in spacer boards. Use ¾-in. spacers as shown.

locked securely in position with the yoke clamp provided.

The radial is not only a useful drum and disc sander, it's a handy router, as you can see in Fig. 13. It takes only a minute to make the conversion. Leave the motor in its vertical position and replace the drum with an accessory router-bit chuck. Set the motor to the desired position to rout the groove, lock it in position, and feed the work slowly. If the groove is more than ⅛ in. deep you'll get a smoother job by cutting to the desired depth in several passes, each not more than about ⅛ in. deep.

In Fig. 14 the radial is set up as a spindle shaper, using an accessory spindle and a three-knife cutterhead of the type used on vertical-spindle shapers. The guard does not come with the accessory spindle; it's improvised from a sheet-metal disc and is not really necessary if one is cautious. In this operation it's best to make the cut in two or more passes for the smoothest work. Feed slowly in either hard or softwood; again, make sure the yoke is securely locked before starting the cut.

A quick conversion makes your radial saw a rotary planer, as in Fig. 15. Use the same two-piece fence as in shaping, change to the router-bit chuck, and fit a rotary planing head. As you can see, it does a smooth, clean job. If you must reduce the thickness of stock more than ⅛ in., make the cuts in two or more passes.

If you don't have the three-knife molding cutter pictured in Fig. 14, you can set up with the three-knife head such as that commonly used for cutting moldings on a table saw. Figs. 16 and 17 show how the setup is made, using the special guard furnished as an accessory. Notice in Fig. 17 that the motor is tilted about 5 degrees from the vertical. For this work you'll need to make the special fence, as shown in the inset detail, to obtain the necessary clearance. The molding shape is similar to that being cut in

WITH THE MOTOR still in the vertical position it's a straight router. If the groove is more than ⅛ in. in depth, cut in two or more passes.

REPLACE ROUTER CHUCK with three-knife shaper cutter and accessory spindle and you have a vertical-spindle shaper. Make the finish cut in two passes.

REPLACE shaping spindle with that for router bit, insert planing head and you have a surfacer. Cuts should not exceed ⅛ in.

A MOLDING HEAD of the type used on the table saw will also work well on most radials. Here the three-knife head is being placed on the motor spindle.

Fig. 14, but of course other molding shapes can be cut with the same setup. In Fig. 18 a panel-raising cut is being made with the same setup, but using a straight knife on the cutterhead rather than the molding knife shown on the head in Fig. 16. You can also do rabbeting with this setup, tilting the motor back to the vertical position. Again the reminder: Don't forget when making any of these setups to lock the yoke firmly in place so that it cannot slide forward or back. And be just as certain that all controls are tight before starting the motor.

Figs. 19 and 20 show dadoing and grooving with a carbide-tipped cutter of the "wobble" type; the width of cut is adjusted by movable "washers" that form the hub. It's a simple gadget easily adjusted for various groove widths, and cuts extremely smoothly on both hard and soft woods. Notice in Fig. 20 that the blade housing has been tilted back so that the rear edge just clears the surface of the stock, as in the ripping

cut with the saw blade; also that the kickback arm has been adjusted for ¾-in. stock.

In Fig. 21 the same type of head pictured in Fig. 20 is being used to make spaced dado cuts in a dentil molding. Here the cuts are spaced by means of a heavy pencil line on the table; if you need greater accuracy, make the special fence in the detail having a fixed stop, the stop entering each successive cut as you move the stock after making the first dado cut.

In ordinary shop work you'll not often be called upon to make a uniform bend in stock. In case you need to make such a bend, Fig. 22 and the inset detail show how it can be done. Once you get the spacing of the successive cuts, as in the detail, mark the location of the cuts on one face of the workpiece and then set the saw blade to cut within about ⅛ in. less than the thickness of the stock. Should it be necessary to hold the workpiece in the curved position until application, Fig. 21, place a few drops of glue in each

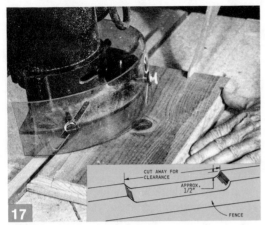

USING HEAD pictured in Fig. 16 and accessory guard permits doing a range of shaping work. When workpieces are small use push stick.

HERE'S A panel-raising job being done with the same head shown in Fig. 16, using a straight cutter. The motor is tilted and the same guard is used.

CUT DADOES from ¼ to ¾ in. with grooving head of the "wobble" type. Adjustments for width are made by rotating washers that form hub.

GROOVES are cut with the same head, the setup made as in ripping cuts. It's well to test for depth on waste stock to assure accuracy. Use the push stick.

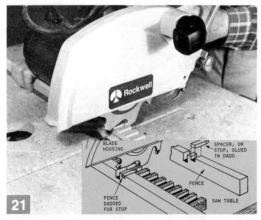

IN MAKING a dentil molding the cuts are simply spaced dadoes. For precise accuracy you can make the special fence shown in the inset detail.

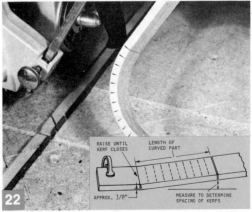

IT'S NOT OFTEN you'll need to bend material by kerfing but the photo and inset detail show how it can be done. Space the kerfs accurately.

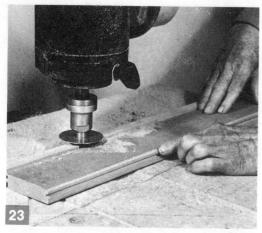

JOINING NARROW pieces to build up to a given width is usually done by doweling but the pros generally prefer to cut a glue joint on the meeting edges.

BY INVERTING the kickback arm in its opening in the housing it can form an additional blade guard for added safety when making repetitive cuts.

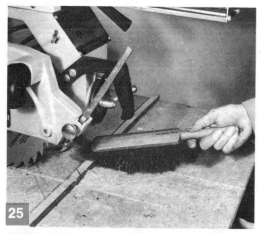

KEEP A BRUSH handy to clear away sawdust that tends to collect in front of the fence. It can cause inaccuracies and may be an operating hazard.

kerf, bend to the full curve and hold in place with clamps until the glue has set.

Home woodworkers generally join pieces edge-to-edge with dowels where it is necessary to build up to a given width with narrow pieces. Many pros prefer to cut glue joints on both edges of the joining pieces. This is easily done on the radial saw by using a three-knife glue-joint cutter and the same molding cutter accessory arbor as that pictured in Fig. 14; also the same two-piece fence. In this job you have to be especially careful to set the cutter to the precise height to cut accurately so that the joining pieces will fit together without any offset at the joining edges. It's best to check the setting by making test cuts on waste stock.

The kickback arm can provide additional guarding of the blade in some operations, such as making a series of repetitive crosscuts. Invert it in its opening and then slide it down so that the end just clears the surface of the stock being cut, as in Fig. 24. In this position it could, conceivably, prevent fingers or even a hand contacting the spinning blade. Make sure that the holding screw is tight and also be sure to replace the arm correctly when changing it back to its original position. On most radials you will have to remove the blade housing to make this change either way.

It's well to check the blade guard occasionally to make sure that all parts, such as the bolts holding the curved parts and the spacer at the back, are properly tightened. Any such metal parts that chance to come loose while the saw is in operation might be caught by the blade and thrown with dangerous force.

A necessary precaution

A final and very necessary precaution is pictured in Fig. 25. Keep a brush handy to clear away sawdust that tends to collect in front of the fence. It not only can cause inaccurate work, but can also be a hazard. It may be a cause of the blade binding suddenly due to the stock being inadvertently tilted. This may stall the motor, damage the material or even cause an injury. And cautious operators who don't wear glasses always wear industrial goggles or a face shield to protect their eyes.

There are, of course, other operations than those shown which can be done on a radial saw, such as novelty cuts, crosshatching with dado cuts and the like.

In any case, a radial saw is one of the most versatile of all shop tools.

Cabinet for your radial-arm saw

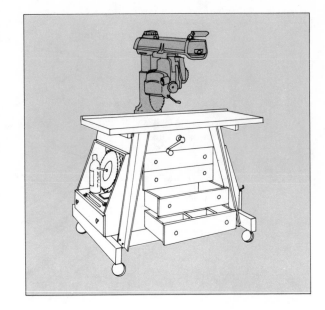

■ THIS CABINET FOR A RADIAL SAW was designed to provide a convenient, attractive and easy-to-keep-clean storage unit that will hold the accessories you need for your saw. The cabinet shown fits beneath a 12-in. radial saw. The overall size can be easily altered to fit any size saw.

To make cleanup a simple chore, cover all exposed parts of the cabinet with plastic laminate. Admittedly, the laminate is a luxury, but the thought of never having to repair a dirt-smeared cabinet more than justifies the cash outlay. If you prefer, the cabinet can be simply painted with an enamel.

How it's built

Constructed of ¾-in. AD plywood, the box is actually symmetrical, with one exception: the top, bottom and sides are edge-rabbeted to receive the ¼-in. hardboard back. Similarly, drawer slides at the back are set in for the back. All edges are flush.

When laying out your cabinet, take all dimensions directly from your radial saw. Then, if any dimensions vary from those shown in the drawing, simply mark the changes right on the drawing and custom-build your cabinet to suit your saw. Also, the dimensions shown do not allow for the laminate, so make certain that you make such allowance if you plan to cover your cabinet.

When laying out your cabinet—and before doing any cutting, rabbeting, or dadoing—double-check the exact location of the four drawers at the front. If you've altered the cabinet dimensions, drawer depths must be adjusted.

The drawers

The amount of drawer space the cabinet provides will surprise you. In fact, there is probably more storage space than you need for radial-saw accessories. You can use the bottom drawer for table-saw items.

For future flexibility, butt-join all divider/partitions. Use ½-in. pine, gluing and nailing them in place after positioning the various accessories in each drawer. Should your requirements ever change, it will be easy to knock out the old dividers and install new ones where you want them. Location of accessories in the drawers is a matter of personal taste and working habits.

The cabinet ends

Since there is space at both ends, you can install a pair of shallow drawers. These are extremely handy for small items such as pencils, tape measures, dividers, and the like that seem to have a way of getting lost in the shuffle when left on the workbench. The perforated board can be left brown (as it comes) and given two coats of varnish. If you paint them, dirt and smudge

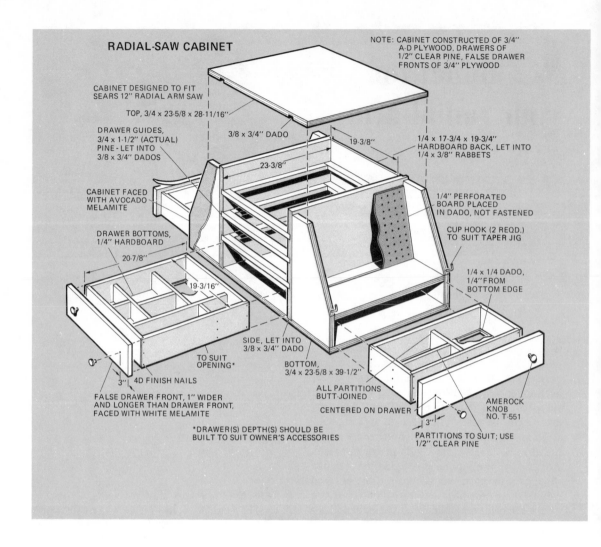

RADIAL-SAW CABINET

NOTE: CABINET CONSTRUCTED OF 3/4"
A-D PLYWOOD, DRAWERS OF
1/2" CLEAR PINE, FALSE DRAWER
FRONTS OF 3/4" PLYWOOD

CABINET DESIGNED TO FIT
SEARS 12" RADIAL ARM SAW

TOP, 3/4 x 23-5/8 x 28-11/16"

3/8 x 3/4" DADO

DRAWER GUIDES,
3/4 x 1-1/2" (ACTUAL)
PINE - LET INTO
3/8 x 3/4" DADOS

19-3/8"

1/4 x 17-3/4 x 19-3/4"
HARDBOARD BACK, LET INTO
1/4 x 3/8" RABBETS

23-3/8"

CABINET FACED
WITH AVOCADO
MELAMITE

1/4" PERFORATED
BOARD PLACED
IN DADO, NOT FASTENED

DRAWER BOTTOMS,
1/4" HARDBOARD

CUP HOOK (2 REQD.)
TO SUIT TAPER JIG

20-7/8"

19-3/16"

1/4 x 1/4 DADO,
1/4" FROM
BOTTOM EDGE

SIDE, LET INTO
3/8 x 3/4" DADO

TO SUIT
OPENING*

BOTTOM,
3/4 x 23-5/8 x 39-1/2"

3" 4D FINISH NAILS

ALL PARTITIONS
BUTT-JOINED

CENTERED ON DRAWER

FALSE DRAWER FRONT, 1" WIDER
AND LONGER THAN DRAWER FRONT,
FACED WITH WHITE MELAMITE

AMEROCK
KNOB
NO. T-551

3"

*DRAWER(S) DEPTH(S) SHOULD BE
BUILT TO SUIT OWNER'S ACCESSORIES

PARTITIONS TO SUIT; USE
1/2" CLEAR PINE

THE ACCESSORY cabinet sits on the base (below) and the whole assembly rides on casters.

ELEVATION
CRANK

2 x 4

2 x 3

3/8 x 2" MACHINE BOLTS
TWO PER LEG. USE ONE
WASHER ON EACH NUT
AND BOLT

NOTCHED

3/8 x 4¼" CARRIAGE BOLT
TO FASTEN FRAME TOGETHER
(4 REQ'D.). USE ONE WASHER
ON EACH NUT AND BOLT

marks will inevitably appear and you will be constantly repainting.

The radial-saw blades are hung on a removable ½-in. dowel. It's good shop practice to use spacers between blades to keep them from dulling one another. (Use 6-in.-dia. circles cut from hardboard.)

The reason both perforated ends are removable is simply one of cleanliness. From time to time, the boards can be lifted out and the dust removed with a vacuum cleaner. To keep sawdust out of the drawers, the back is fitted with ¼-in. hardboard.

Even if the number of radial-saw accessories you currently own is limited, this cabinet should be a welcome addition to your shop. While you're building your accessory collection, you can use that valuable drawer space for almost any kind of storage.

Removable perforated panels

SAW BLADES hang on a removable ½-in. dowel in the left end of the cabinet with separators.

PERFORATED boards aren't fastened permanently in place, but rest in dadoes as in the top sketch.

THE DOWEL'S block must be located with care; your blades' size will dictate its proper position.

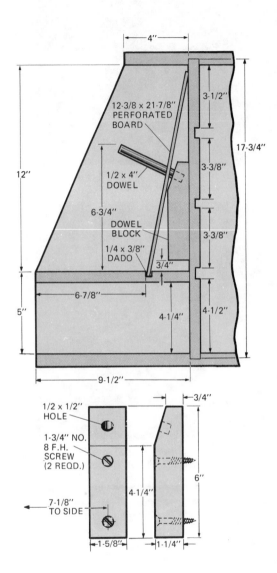

Flexible drawer layouts

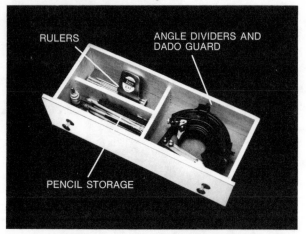

RULERS

ANGLE DIVIDERS AND DADO GUARD

PENCIL STORAGE

THE END drawer is shallow, ideal for frequently used items such as a tape measure and pencils.

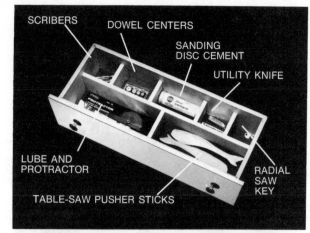

SCRIBERS

DOWEL CENTERS

SANDING DISC CEMENT

UTILITY KNIFE

LUBE AND PROTRACTOR

RADIAL SAW KEY

TABLE-SAW PUSHER STICKS

DRAWER at the other end holds more miscellaneous equipment, including the table-saw push sticks.

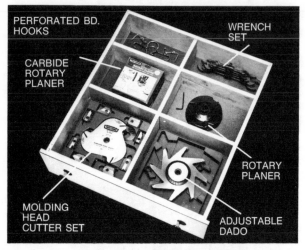

PERFORATED BD. HOOKS

WRENCH SET

CARBIDE ROTARY PLANER

ROTARY PLANER

MOLDING HEAD CUTTER SET

ADJUSTABLE DADO

TOP FRONT drawer gets the most-used accessories plus such small items as the wrench set and hooks.

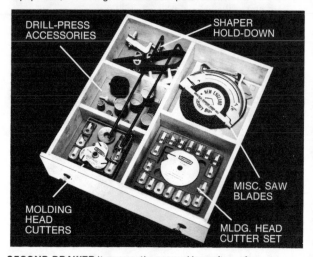

DRILL-PRESS ACCESSORIES

SHAPER HOLD-DOWN

MISC. SAW BLADES

MOLDING HEAD CUTTERS

MLDG. HEAD CUTTER SET

SECOND-DRAWER items are those used less often—for masonry- and metal-cutting blades, for example.

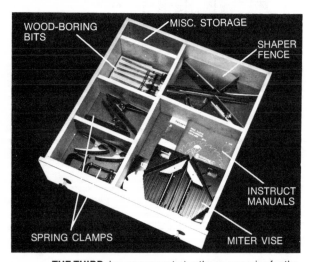

WOOD-BORING BITS

MISC. STORAGE

SHAPER FENCE

INSTRUCT MANUALS

SPRING CLAMPS

MITER VISE

THE THIRD drawer concentrates the accessories for the saw's conversion to use as a drill press.

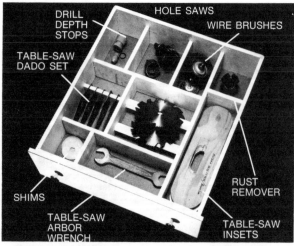

DRILL DEPTH STOPS

HOLE SAWS

WIRE BRUSHES

TABLE-SAW DADO SET

SHIMS

RUST REMOVER

TABLE-SAW ARBOR WRENCH

TABLE-SAW INSETS

BOTTOM DRAWER keeps the bulk of the table-saw items together in one organized collection.

THIS RADIAL-SAW CABINET may be one of the best ones designed. In addition to its folding tables, it boasts a repetitive-stop feature, sawdust chute and drawer, and blade storage.

Table for a radial-arm saw

■ THERE ARE SEVERAL reasons why this is one of the best saw cabinets you'll ever see. First, it's really well built. Oak and birch plywood was used to construct the prototype, but the design is so sound you can economize by substituting fir and fir plywood. Second, the sawdust deflector chute and easy-to-empty drawer constitute a neat, simple solution to the dunes of sawdust that usually accumulate in and around a saw. Third, the cabinet has a built-in blade organizer. It will store 12 blades, a dado head and a molding head, plus other tools such as tape measures and squares that you might like to keep at your saw station. Fourth, the entire unit moves on casters,

two of which are equipped with locks to make the unit stable.

The list doesn't stop here. The extension tables let you handle long boards with ease. Each is equipped with a pair of stops. Repetitive stops, which slide on top of the tracks, are used with boards that do not extend beyond the ends of the tables. Extension stop bars, with dowel catches at outboard ends, slide under the surface between the angle irons and can be used when the workpiece extends beyond the end of the tables. The topside stop will lock at any point along the track when you simply tighten a wingnut. The extension stop-bar locks in place by tightening a rubber-surfaced friction clamp.

Best of all, the extension tables fold up neatly accordion style, freeing up shop space when you need it. In the open position, the extension tables provide a valuable working surface for assembling projects.

The cabinet stiles and rails, along with the dadoes, rabbets and grooves indicated in the plans are cut first. (See materials list for saw cabinet.) Then assemble the sides with carriage bolts and glue. Join the two sides with the rails, using

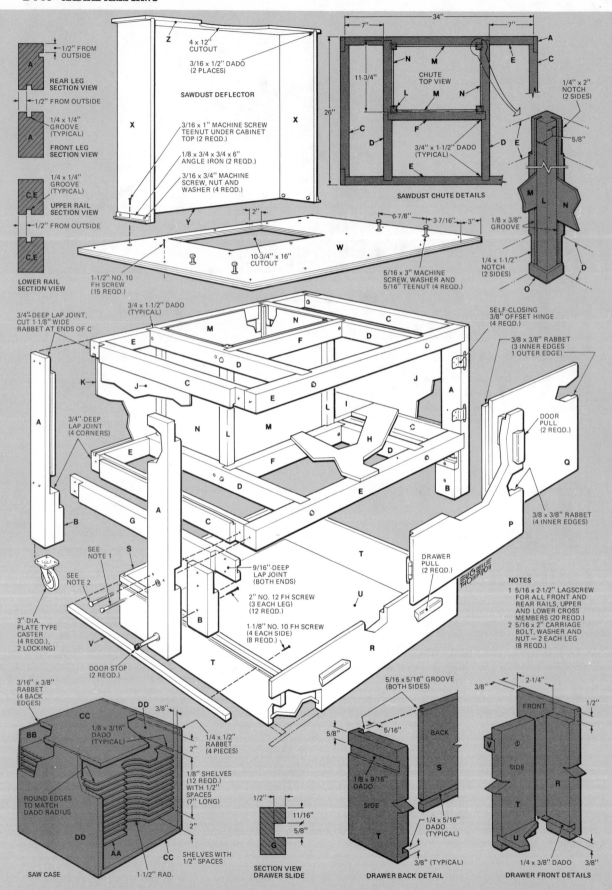

REAR LEG SECTION VIEW

1/2" FROM OUTSIDE

1/2" FROM OUTSIDE

FRONT LEG SECTION VIEW

1/4 x 1/4" GROOVE (TYPICAL)

UPPER RAIL SECTION VIEW

1/4 x 1/4" GROOVE (TYPICAL)

1/2" FROM OUTSIDE

LOWER RAIL SECTION VIEW

Z

4 x 12" CUTOUT

3/16 x 1/2" DADO (2 PLACES)

SAWDUST DEFLECTOR

X

3/16 x 1" MACHINE SCREW TEENUT UNDER CABINET TOP (2 REQD.)

1/8 x 3/4 x 3/4 x 6" ANGLE IRON (2 REQD.)

3/16 x 3/4" MACHINE SCREW, NUT AND WASHER (4 REQD.)

X

Y

2"

10-3/4" x 16" CUTOUT

W

6-7/8" 3-7/16" 3"

5/16 x 3" MACHINE SCREW, WASHER AND 5/16" TEENUT (4 REQD.)

34"

7" 7"

A

N M E C

11-3/4" CHUTE TOP VIEW

L M N

C F

D E D

3/4" x 1-1/2" DADO (TYPICAL)

26"

E

SAWDUST CHUTE DETAILS

1/4" x 2" NOTCH (2 SIDES)

5/8"

M L N

1/8 x 3/8" GROOVE

1/4 x 1-1/2" NOTCH (2 SIDES)

O

D

1-1/2" NO. 10 FH SCREW (15 REQD.)

3/4"-DEEP LAP JOINT, CUT 1-1/8" WIDE RABBET AT ENDS OF C

3/4 x 1-1/2" DADO (TYPICAL)

M N C

E D

K

J C A

A

3/4"-DEEP LAP JOINT (4 CORNERS)

N L M

E

F D

A

G C

SEE NOTE 1

S

SEE NOTE 2

9/16"-DEEP LAP JOINT (BOTH ENDS)

2" NO. 12 FH SCREW (3 EACH LEG) (12 REQD.)

B

1-1/8" NO. 10 FH SCREW (4 EACH SIDE) (8 REQD.)

3" DIA. PLATE TYPE CASTER (4 REQD.), 2 LOCKING)

V

DOOR STOP (2 REQD.)

B

T

L I

H D

E

B

A

SELF-CLOSING 3/8" OFFSET HINGE (4 REQD.)

3/8 x 3/8" RABBET (3 INNER EDGES 1 OUTER EDGE)

DOOR PULL (2 REQD.)

Q

3/8 x 3/8" RABBET (4 INNER EDGES)

P

DRAWER PULL (2 REQD.)

T

U

R

NOTES

1 5/16 x 2-1/2" LAGSCREW FOR ALL FRONT AND REAR RAILS, UPPER AND LOWER CROSS MEMBERS (20 REQD.)

2 5/16 x 2" CARRIAGE BOLT, WASHER AND NUT — 2 EACH LEG (8 REQD.)

3/16" x 3/8" RABBET (4 BACK EDGES)

BB

CC

DD

3/8"

1/8 x 3/16" DADO (TYPICAL)

1/4 x 1/2" RABBET (4 PIECES)

2"

1/8" SHELVES (12 REQD.) WITH 1/2" SPACES (7" LONG)

2"

ROUND EDGES TO MATCH DADO RADIUS

DD

AA

CC

SHELVES WITH 1/2" SPACES

1-1/2" RAD.

SAW CASE

1/2"

11/16"

5/8"

G

SECTION VIEW DRAWER SLIDE

5/16 x 5/16" GROOVE (BOTH SIDES)

5/16"

BACK

5/8"

1/8 x 9/16" DADO

SIDE

S

T

1/4 x 5/16" DADO (TYPICAL)

3/8" (TYPICAL)

DRAWER BACK DETAIL

2-1/4"

3/8"

FRONT

1/2"

V

SIDE

R

T

U

1/4 x 3/8" DADO

3/8"

DRAWER FRONT DETAILS

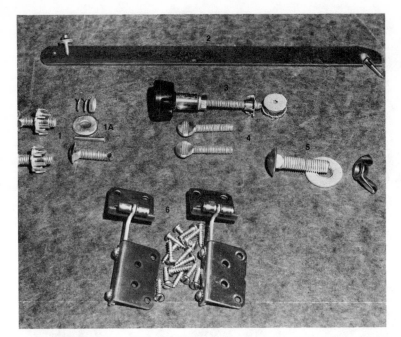

HARDWARE NEEDED: (1) ⅜x2-in. carriage bolts, Teenuts—for leg-height adjusters. (1-A) ⅜x⅜x2-in. carriage bolt with two sides ground and ⅛-in. hole drilled through thread end to receive ⅛-in. steel pin, ⅜-in. washer and section of extension spring—to make leg-locking device. (2) ⅛x1x14-in. strap iron with screw, washer—for leg brace. Bore ³/₁₆-in. hole in frame and cut locking slot in leg end. (3) Knob, ⁵/₁₆x3-in. threaded rod, lock washer, nut, ⁵/₁₆-in. Teenut, ⅞-in.-dia. x ½-in. dowel with nonslip self-adhesive stair tread. Assemble as shown in plans—device functions as friction lock when extension stop bar is in use. (4) ⁵/₁₆x2½-in. thumbscrews may be used in extension stop bar locking device in place of knob and threaded rod assembly. (5) ½x1½-in. carriage bolt with washer and wingnut. Assemble through stop bar to function as a lock. (6) Drop-leaf table hinges, screws. Hinges allow leg assembly to fold against top of table.

MATERIALS LIST—SAW CABINET

KEY	PCS.	SIZE AND DESCRIPTION
A	4	1½ x 2⅝ x 23″ oak
B	4	1⅛ x 2⅝ x 6½″ oak
C	4	1½ x 2 x 23″ oak
D	4	1½ x 2 x 24½″ oak
E	4	1½ x 2 x 34″ oak
F	4	1½ x 2 x 18½″ oak
G	2	1⅛ x 2 x 26″ oak
H	1	⅜ x 12¾ x 34″ fir plywood
I	2	⅜ x 8½ x 11¾″ fir plywood
J	2	¼ x 13 x 21¼″ birch plywood
K	1	¼ x 13 x 33″ birch plywood
L	4	1⅛ x 1⅛ x 16″
M	2	⅛ x 15⅞ x 16″ tempered hardboard
N	2	⅛ x 10⅝ x 16″ tempered hardboard
O	4	½ x 1 x 1″ plywood
P	1	¾ x 13⅛ x 16⅝″ birch plywood
Q	1	¾ x 13⅛ x 16¹⁵/₁₆″ birch plywood
R	1	¾ x 6¾ x 33¼″ birch plywood
S	1	⅝ x 6¼ x 29¼″ fir plywood
T	2	⅝ x 6¼ x 25¼″ fir plywood
U	1	¼ x 24⅝ x 29¼″ fir plywood
V	2	⁹/₁₆ x ¾ x 25¼″ oak
W	1	¾ x 27 x 38″ birch plywood
X	2	½ x 6 x 24″ fir plywood
Y	1	⅛ x 24 x 27″ tempered hardboard
Z	1	½ x 6 x 29″ fir plywood
AA	12	⅛ x 10½ x 11″ tempered hardboard
BB	1	⅛ x 11½ x 11¾″ fir plywood
CC	2	½ x 11¼ x 11⅛″ fir plywood
DD	2	½ x 12 x 11⅛″ fir plywood

Misc.: 4, drawer and door pulls; 4, ⅜″ offset self-closing hinges; 20, ⁵/₁₆ x 2½″ lagscrews; 8, ⁵/₁₆ x 2″ carriage bolts washers, nuts; 2, ⅛x¾x¾x6″ angle irons; 2, ³/₁₆ x 1″ machine screws and Teenuts; 4, ³/₁₆ x ¾″ machine screws, nuts and washers; 4, 3″-dia. plate-type casters (2 locking and 2 nonlocking); 2 stem-type door stops; 4, ⁵/₁₆″ machine screws and 4, ⁵/₁₆″ Teenuts; screws, nails and brads as required.

MATERIALS LIST—EXTENSION TABLE

KEY	PCS.	SIZE AND DESCRIPTION
A	2	1½ x 1¾ x 32″ oak
B	2	¾ x 2 x 21¼″ oak
D	1	⅛ x ¾ x 13½″ strap iron
E	1	¾ x 8 x 17″ birch plywood
F	1	¾ x 2¾ x 17″ birch plywood
G	1	¾ x 2½ x 17″ birch plywood
H	2	1 x 2 x 32″ oak
I	1	½ x 1¼ x 31 ⁷/₁₆″ oak
J	1	¾ x 2 x 15¾″ oak
K	2	1½ x 2 x 17″ oak
L	1	¾ x 2 x 6″ oak
M	1	¾ x 10⅞ x 32″ birch plywood
N	1	¾ x 8 x 32″ birch plywood
O	2	¼ x ¾ x 32″ oak
P	1	¾ x 2 x 23″ oak
Q	1	¾ x 2 x 2″ oak
R	1	⁹/₁₆ x 1¾ x 32″ oak

Misc.: 2, ⅛ x ¾ x ¾ x 32″ angle iron; 2, ⁵/₁₆ x 3″ carriage bolts, washers and nuts; 2, 1⅝ x 2″ butt hinges; 2″ hanger bolt, washer and wingnut; 2, ⅜ x 1½″ carriage bolt; 2, ⅜″ Teenuts; ⁵/₁₆″ Teenut; ⁵/₁₆ x 3″ threaded rod; knob; 2, ³/₁₆″ bolts and Teenuts; ½ x 2″ carriage bolt washer and wingnut; ½ x 1½″ dowel; ⅞-dia. x ½″ dowel; ⅞-dia. rubber disc cut from stair tread.

lagscrews and glue. It's a good idea to square and clamp the entire unit before bolting and screwing it together.

Next, make the four corner stabilizers of the sawdust chute and screw them in place. Add panel stops (O) and slip the four tempered hardboard panels into the grooves from the top.

Install the floor of the cabinet around the chute in three sections (I, I and J). Then attach the birch plywood at top; countersink screw heads.

Once the basic cabinet frame is complete, turn your attention to appendages like the sawdust deflector, dust-collecting drawer and the heavy duty plate-type casters. Assemble the housing with nails and glue. Two pieces of angle iron are used to attach the deflector to the cabinet top. Bolt the angle iron to the deflector with machine screws or stovebolts, washers and nuts. Use Teenuts, however, when attaching the assembled

SAW CABINET can be used—or easily moved to a new location—with the extension tables folded.

LEG-LOCKING device holds the leg assembly securely to the angle-iron track when the table is folded.

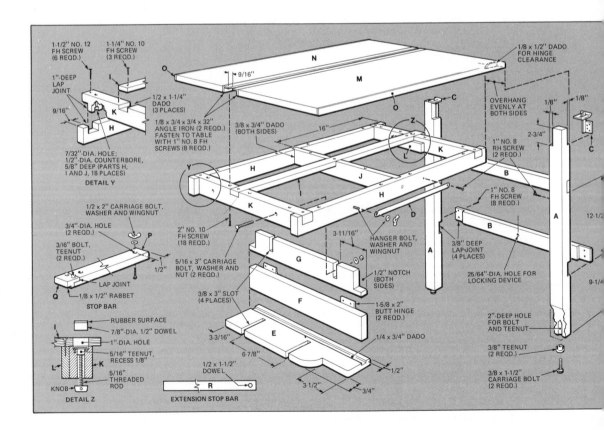

1-1/2" NO. 12 FH SCREW (6 REQD.)

1-1/4" NO. 10 FH SCREW (3 REQD.)

1"-DEEP LAP JOINT

9/16"

1/2 x 1-1/4" DADO (3 PLACES)

1/8 x 3/4 x 3/4 x 32" ANGLE IRON (2 REQD.) FASTEN TO TABLE WITH 1" NO. 8 FH SCREWS (8 REQD.)

7/32"-DIA. HOLE; 1/2"-DIA. COUNTERBORE, 5/8" DEEP (PARTS H, I AND J, 18 PLACES)

DETAIL Y

1/2 x 2" CARRIAGE BOLT, WASHER AND WINGNUT

3/4"-DIA. HOLE (2 REQD.)

3/16" BOLT, TEENUT (2 REQD.)

LAP JOINT

1/2"

1/8 x 1/2" RABBET

STOP BAR

RUBBER SURFACE

7/8"-DIA. 1/2" DOWEL

1"-DIA. HOLE

5/16" TEENUT, RECESS 1/8"

5/16" THREADED ROD

KNOB

DETAIL Z

9/16"

N

M

O

3/8 x 3/4" DADO (BOTH SIDES)

16"

Z

K

L

H

J

H

Y

I

K

2" NO. 10 FH SCREW (18 REQD.)

5/16 x 3" CARRIAGE BOLT, WASHER AND NUT (2 REQD.)

3/8 x 3" SLOT (4 PLACES)

G

F

E

3-3/16"

6-7/8"

1/2 x 1-1/2" DOWEL

R

EXTENSION STOP BAR

3-1/2"

3/4"

HANGER BOLT, WASHER AND WINGNUT

1/2" NOTCH (BOTH SIDES)

3-11/16"

D

A

1-5/8 x 2" BUTT HINGE (2 REQD.)

1/4 x 3/4" DADO

1/2"

C

1/8 x 1/2" DADO FOR HINGE CLEARANCE

OVERHANG EVENLY AT BOTH SIDES

1/8"   1/8"

2-3/4"

1" NO. 8 RH SCREW (2 REQD.)

B

1" NO. 8 FH SCREW (8 REQD.)

3/8" DEEP LAP-JOINT (4 PLACES)

25/64"-DIA. HOLE FOR LOCKING DEVICE

C

A

12-1/2

9-1/4

2"-DEEP HOLE FOR BOLT AND TEENUT

3/8" TEENUT (2 REQD.)

3/8 x 1-1/2" CARRIAGE BOLT (2 REQD.)

B

P

Q

I

L

K

deflector to the cabinet top. This will make it easy to remove when the need arises. To install the Teenuts, drill ¼-in. holes in the cabinet top. Hold the Teenut under the hole and thread on a bolt from the topside. Then tighten down on the bolt to pull the Teenut prongs into the plywood. Teenuts can be installed in the conventional manner if you lay out, mark and drill holes before fastening the top.

When building the drawer, fasten the oak runners to the grooves in the drawer sides with screws driven from the inside out. Add oak slides (G) and slide supports (B) to the front and rear stiles. Later, after the finish has been applied, a liberal application of paraffin to the slides will make the drawer move with a good deal more ease.

Cut the rabbets for the cabinet doors and mount them on the cabinet with self-closing hinges for both convenience and safety.

Building the extension tables

You may choose to build one or both extension tables. If you choose one, make it the right side, since it generally gets the most use. As with the cabinet, any good solid wood can be used. (See materials list for single extension table.)

Cut the legs and rails first, with notches and dadoes as shown. Note that it will be necessary to reverse one of the drop-leaf hinges—the mortise must be cut accordingly. Bore holes in the ends of the legs for the table height adjustment; install Teenut and carriage bolt. Also bore holes to accommodate the leg lock and extension stop clamp. Next, cut the two surface sections to size and cut slots for hinge clearance. Fasten lengths of angle iron to edges with screws and then install top by driving screws up through the rails.

Not necessarily adjustable

The assembly which joins the table to the cabinet does not necessarily have to be adjustable. The attachment may be made with bolts through bored holes instead of slots. This one was made adjustable, so that it would be possible to change over to a different saw with a different table and base dimensions at a later date.

Make the stop bar and extension stop bar as shown in the plans and install all remaining hardware. Note that the leg lock (see photo, parts 1A) secures the table legs to the underside of the table surface. To make the lock, grind the carriage-bolt head flat on two sides. Drill a ⅛-in.-dia. hole in the threaded end of the bolt to receive a pin cut from a 10d nail. When installed, a 90° turn of the pin will lock the underground edges behind the angle-iron track.

The extension stop bar clamp (see detail Z) is used only with the extension stop bar. Cover the clamp's pressure plate with a ⅞-in.-dia. piece of rubber—which may be cut from nonslip stair tread or any similar piece of rubber—to increase its grip.

Mounting and positioning saw

In the prototype, we installed De Walt's 770, 10-inch Deluxe model radial saw—although other saws with a steel base and column mount can also be used. The radial saw base was centered with its front flush to the cabinet front and then bolted in place through the cabinet top. In this position, the extension table tracks for the sliding stops will be just forward of the saw fence. With different saws there may be a slightly different location for mounting the extension table to the cabinet. There is adequate room to make this adjustment comfortably.

Molding head fence for a radial saw

FENCE FITS FLUSH in table in place of saw's own fence and rear table board, which you remove. Hold-down fixtures shown can be bought separately.

■ USED WITH a molding head, this adjustable fence assembly makes your radial-arm saw perform like a real wood shaper. It drops in place flush with the table surface and occupies the area behind the saw's fence. You remove both fence and rear table board when you want to use it. Total thickness of the base must equal thickness of the saw's wood table. The ⅛-in. hardboard covering on the bottom of the fence provides for free movement over the table.

The square opening in the base provides clearance for the motor arbor and vertical cutter ad-justment. Two ⅜x1½-in. capscrews, washers and Teenuts are used to lock the movable fence in place. Use oak for the two fences and rabbet the edges. The rest is made of fir plywood. Glue and clamp the tempered hardboard to the surfaces indicated.

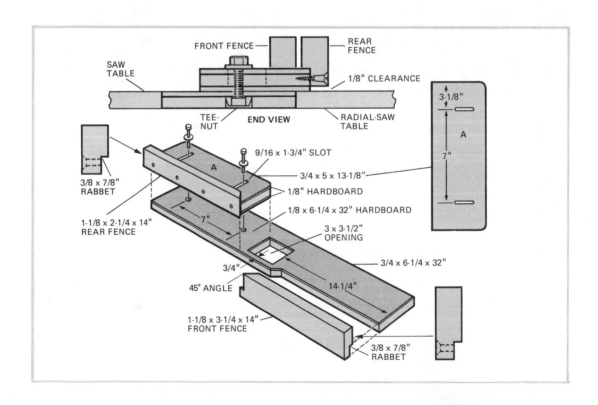

NO-NONSENSE, 16-ft. radial-arm saw bench has flip-away fence for oversize ripping. Generous-size drawers and storage tray offer space for accessories and in-progress work. Hefty casters make bench mobile and easy to align.

Bench with lots of storage

■ A RADIAL-ARM saw bench that's close to being perfection can be yours by building this version for half the price of commercial models. Drawers, cabinet front, cross members and tray edges are of 1-in. spruce stock. Drawer bottoms and cabinet sides are AC (good-one-side) plywood. The top surface is cut from a 4x10-ft. sheet of 1⅛-in. particleboard. Hardwood ties stabilize legs.

To begin, build the base, which has a front and rear rail, and eight connecting cross members glued into the dadoed rails. Clamp overnight. Notch the back rail and set ledgers at the correct height for your saw. Attach the eight legs, after checking that each measures exactly 32 in. from the top of its respective rail to the floor. In other words, the lap joint at the top of each leg must be set 2 in. below the rail's top edge. Next, glue and clamp the cabinet front, sides and back (½-in. AC plywood) into previously routed grooves in legs and bottom edges of rails.

Dress the fronts, sides and backs of the drawers to ½ in. and lay out as in drawing. The fronts may be rabbeted flush to their openings and dovetailed to sides, or built with butt joints and a screwed-on false front. (Use 2d nails and white glue at butt joints and ¾-in. No. 6 fh screws with white glue to attach the false front.) Pulls and

CONSTRUCTION DRAWING

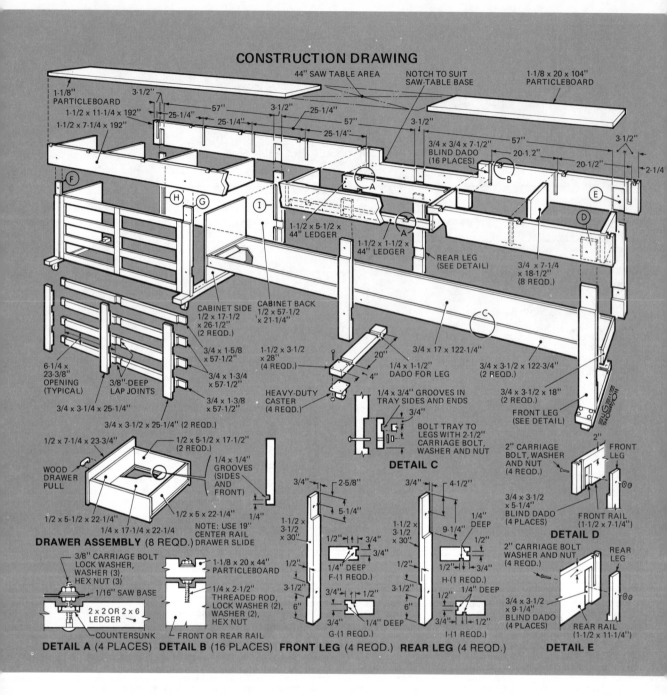

44" SAW TABLE AREA

NOTCH TO SUIT SAW-TABLE BASE

1-1/8 x 20 x 104" PARTICLEBOARD

1-1/8" PARTICLEBOARD

3-1/2"

1-1/2 x 11-1/4 x 192"

1-1/2 7-1/4 x 192"

25-1/4"

57"

3-1/2"

25-1/4"

25-1/4"

57"

25-1/4"

3-1/2"

3/4 x 3/4 x 7-1/2" BLIND DADO (16 PLACES)

57"

3-1/2"

20-1.2"

20-1/2"

2-1/4

1-1/2 x 5-1/2 x 44" LEDGER

1-1/2 x 1-1/2 x 44" LEDGER

REAR LEG (SEE DETAIL)

3/4 x 7-1/4 x 18-1/2" (8 REQD.)

F

H

G

I

A

A

B

E

D

CABINET SIDE 1/2 x 17-1/2 x 26-1/2" (2 REQD.)

CABINET BACK 1/2 x 57-1/2 x 21-1/4"

3/4 x 1-5/8 x 57-1/2"

1-1/2 x 3-1/2 x 28" (4 REQD.)

20"

3/4 x 17 x 122-1/4"

3/4 x 3-1/2 x 122-3/4" (2 REQD.)

6-1/4 x 23-3/8" OPENING (TYPICAL)

3/8"-DEEP LAP JOINTS

3/4 x 1-3/4 x 57-1/2"

1/4 x 1-1/2" DADO FOR LEG

4"

3/4 x 3-1/2 x 18" (2 REQD.)

3/4 x 3-1/4 x 25-1/4"

3/4 x 1-3/8 x 57-1/2"

HEAVY-DUTY CASTER (4 REQD.)

1/4 x 3/4" GROOVES IN TRAY SIDES AND ENDS

3/4"

FRONT LEG (SEE DETAIL)

3/4 x 3-1/2 x 25-1/4" (2 REQD.)

BOLT TRAY TO LEGS WITH 2-1/2" CARRIAGE BOLT, WASHER AND NUT

DETAIL C

2" CARRIAGE BOLT, WASHER AND NUT (4 REQD.)

2"

FRONT LEG

1/2 x 7-1/4 x 23-3/4"

1/2 x 5-1/2 x 17-1/2" (2 REQD.)

1/4 x 1/4" GROOVES (SIDES AND FRONT)

3/4 x 3-1/2 x 5-1/4" BLIND DADO (4 PLACES)

WOOD DRAWER PULL

3/4"

2-5/8"

3/4"

4-1/2"

1/4" DEEP

FRONT RAIL (1-1/2 x 7-1/4")

DETAIL D

1/2 x 5-1/2 x 22-1/4"

1/2 x 5 x 22-1/4"

5-1/4"

1-1/2 3-1/2 x 30"

1-1/2 3-1/2 x 30"

9-1/4"

1/2"

2" CARRIAGE BOLT WASHER AND NUT (4 REQD.)

REAR LEG

1/4 x 17-1/4 x 22-1/4

1/4"

NOTE: USE 19" CENTER RAIL DRAWER SLIDE

1/2"

3/4"

1/4" DEEP F-(1 REQD.)

3/4"

1/2"

1/4" DEEP

3/4"

3/4 x 3-1/2 x 9-1/4" BLIND DADO (4 PLACES)

DRAWER ASSEMBLY (8 REQD.)

3/8" CARRIAGE BOLT LOCK WASHER, WASHER (3), HEX NUT (3)

1-1/16" SAW BASE

2 x 2 OR 2 x 6 LEDGER

COUNTERSUNK

DETAIL A (4 PLACES)

1-1/8 x 20 x 44" PARTICLEBOARD

1/4 x 2-1/2" THREADED ROD, LOCK WASHER (2), WASHER (2), HEX NUT

FRONT OR REAR RAIL

DETAIL B (16 PLACES)

3-1/2"

6"

3/4"

1/2"

1/4" DEEP G-(1 REQD.)

FRONT LEG (4 REQD.)

H-(1 REQD.)

3-1/2"

6"

1/2"

3/4"

1/2"

1/4" DEEP I-(1 REQD.)

REAR LEG (4 REQD.)

REAR RAIL (1-1/2 x 11-1/4")

DETAIL E

---

slides used are the single-channel, three-roller type—standard hardware items.

Construct the storage tray separately. Slip the bottom into ¼-in.-deep grooves in the 1x4 sides and join at corners. Simple butt joints will do, but you can use dovetails for extra strength. Fit the completed tray component into previously cut leg notches.

Now add hardwood ties to the leg bottoms, with ample projection for heavy-duty casters. Secure casters with ¼x3½-in. lagbolts threaded into previously embedded ⅜-in.-dia. dowels.

When you need a wide rip or extra-wide crosscut, you can lift the hinged fence extensions, adjust your saw (including moving its central fence to the rear position) and begin ripping. To construct, mortise for and glue six hardwood mounting blocks into the particleboard table extensions to obtain solid hinge mounts. Position as on surface plan. Cut the six hardwood fence extensions and carefully countersink for a 1x⅜-in.-dia. carriage bolt through the center of the routed lap. Hinge fence extensions to the mounting blocks.

Making the fences

The fences are made from a straight 14-ft. piece of 1x6 clear pine cut in 104-in. and 44-in. lengths. Rip a 3-in. width off the two pieces for the two fence bases. Then rip a 2-in.-wide strip from each remaining piece for the two fences and join these pieces to bases with tongue-and-groove joints. The lip between fence bottom and the underside of its base should equal the gap between hinge leaves (see detail) or the fence will not sit at 90° to the table.

Center and cut six slits into the completed fence sections. Flip the sections and rout out six recesses for corresponding hardwood extensions. Secure fences to extensions with bolts, washers and nuts.

To align, start by leveling the bench, using the storage tray as a base. Set up your saw according to manufacturer's instructions; then level the saw table by raising or lowering the nuts on the saw lifts. Carefully level each table extension to the tabletop. Gently move the saw and the two extensions into alignment. Check alignment of fence sections with a long piece of black thread. Tighten nuts firmly on saw lifts, extension lifts and fence adjustments.

Adapting bench for your saw

This bench is designed around a Craftsman 12-in. radial-arm saw, but you can adapt it to almost any other model. The critical changes depend on the saw-base dimensions and adjustment-crank positions. Saw-base ledgers and the saw-base notch in the rear rail would be most likely to need modification. Carefully study your particular saw and your needs before you begin construction.

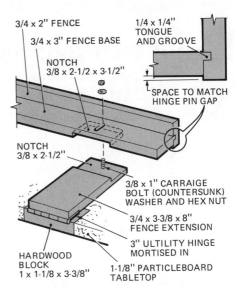

FENCE EXTENSION DETAIL

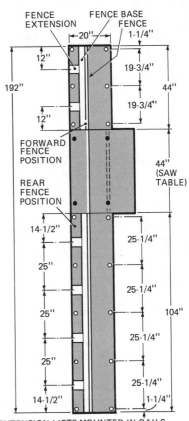

o EXTENSION LIFTS MOUNTED IN RAILS
• SAW LIFTS MOUNTED THROUGH LEDGERS

SURFACE PLAN

ARRANGE saw lifts at the corners of your saw base to suit, and extension lifts according to the plan above. Saw 16 2½-in. lengths of ¼-in. threaded rod for latter—it costs less than sawing off bolt heads.

Table extensions for a radial saw

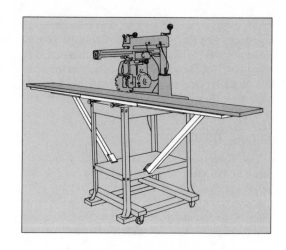

■ WHEN YOU'RE CUTTING long boards, the weight of the outboard section often makes the sawing operation a dangerous one. To avoid an accident under those conditions, a radial-saw table may be rigged with a pair of fold-down extensions. With proper support under those extra-long workpieces, cutting is a snap.

The extensions shown were made of plywood built up to match table thickness. Hinged to the saw table, they drop down when not needed, yet automatically engage when raised into position.

To fasten them to the saw table, lay a long board across and clamp the extensions to it. Use wood screws to attach them, and, if necessary,

shim under the hinges to make the extensions flush with the tabletop. Notice in the drawing that the supports are offset 2 inches so that they pass each other when in the folded position.

DOUBLED-UP ½-in. plywood was used in these fold-down extensions to match the original table's thickness. You can shim the hinges if necessary.

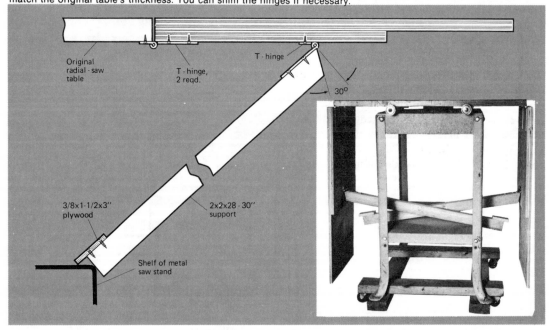

Original radial - saw table

T - hinge, 2 reqd.

T - hinge

30°

3/8x1-1/2x3'' plywood

2x2x28 - 30'' support

Shelf of metal saw stand

Jacks quickly level a radial-saw table

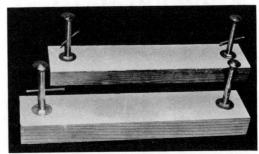

TWO PIECES of 2x4 (18 in. long) have ½ x 5-in. carriage bolts turned into holes at the ends and locked in place with nuts and washers. The cross handles in the bolts are simply nails—optional but handy.

■ THE IMPORTANCE of a perfectly level table is obvious in the case of a radial-arm saw. If the fixed table runs "downhill," rabbets and dadoes will run downhill and vary in thickness from one end to the other. Only when the table surface is level with the saw's overarm will the saw cut rabbets and dadoes right on the button.

The best way to check the table on your saw is with these leveling jacks. To use them you loosen the four bolts that hold the slotted rails, set the jacks in place as in the drawing, lock the motor in a vertical position and then move the motor and arm over the entire surface. When the motor shaft lightly touches the surface at all points, the table will be level. A slight turn of the jacks will correct any variance.

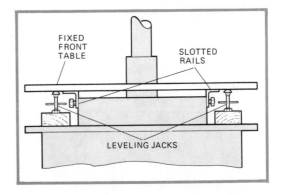

FIXED FRONT TABLE

SLOTTED RAILS

LEVELING JACKS

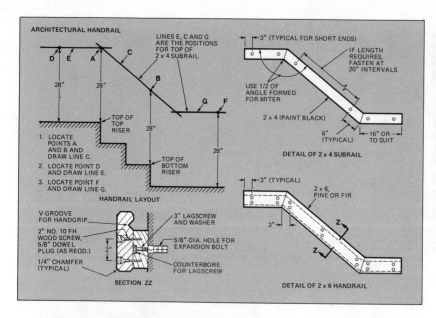

ARCHITECTURAL HANDRAIL

LINES E, C AND G ARE THE POSITIONS FOR TOP OF 2 x 4 SUBRAIL

28" 28"

TOP OF TOP RISER

28"

28"

TOP OF BOTTOM RISER

1. LOCATE POINTS A AND B AND DRAW LINE C.
2. LOCATE POINT D AND DRAW LINE E.
3. LOCATE POINT F AND DRAW LINE G.

HANDRAIL LAYOUT

V-GROOVE FOR HANDGRIP

2" NO. 10 FH WOOD SCREW, 5/8" DOWEL PLUG (AS REQD.)

1/4" CHAMFER (TYPICAL)

SECTION ZZ

3" LAGSCREW AND WASHER

5/8"-DIA. HOLE FOR EXPANSION BOLT

COUNTERBORE FOR LAGSCREW

3" (TYPICAL FOR SHORT ENDS)

IF LENGTH REQUIRES, FASTEN AT 20" INTERVALS

USE 1/2 OF ANGLE FORMED FOR MITER

2 x 4 (PAINT BLACK)

6" (TYPICAL)   16" OR TO SUIT

DETAIL OF 2 x 4 SUBRAIL

3" (TYPICAL)

2 x 6, PINE OR FIR

3"

Z

Z

DETAIL OF 2 x 6 HANDRAIL

HANDRAIL adds safety and an attractive touch to a home. Note the finger grip in detail.

Handrail to enhance your home

■ MANY TWO- and three-step entry stairs don't have handrails. Using stairs in icy weather can be dangerous, especially for oldsters.

If your steps run parallel to a wall, you can get the jump on safety by building the handsome handrail pictured. It's a good alternative to installing a standard wrought-iron rail. Painted or given a clear, polyurethane finish, the handrail lends a pleasing, substantial finishing touch to your entry.

Begin work on the handrail by drawing a line to indicate the top of the 2x4 subrail on the wall. Use the 28-in. standard banister height shown. Cut the pieces to length to suit your needs. Once you determine the joining angle, the remainder of the job is easy. Measure lengths off line drawn and cut the three 2x4 segments with desired angles.

In a masonry wall, use masonry bits to bore ⅝-in.-dia. holes for expansion bolts by first boring 3/16-in., then ⅜-in. and finally the ⅝-in.-dia. holes. Countersink lagscrews in the subrail. In walls made of other material drive countersunk hefty wood screws into studs if you have vinyl or aluminum siding.

Use a bevel square to transfer the angle already determined onto the 2x6-in. handrail pieces and cut. Since this rail is set ¼ in. below the 2x4 bottom, the ends of the pieces will project slightly past the subrail.

Chamfer (bevel) 2x6 edges for hand comfort; rout, shape or saw the backs, above the 2x4, to make a finger grip. Space the fastening screws so they don't hit subrail fasteners. Add dowel plugs and apply finish.

Wrought-iron railing installation

NEWEL POSTS are used for the end posts, corner posts and intermediate posts. The number required is determined by the overall size of the stoop. A stoop that is the same width as the steps generally requires four posts. A stoop wider than the steps can require as many as six or more posts. Posts are anchored to the masonry stoop and steps by flanges that are attached with expansion bolts inserted in predrilled holes. A concrete bit is used to drill the holes for the bolts.

AFTER THE NEWEL POSTS are in place, preassembled, adjustable rail sections are marked for length. Here in order to maintain uniform spacing of spindles, excess length is cut from each end of the upper and lower rails. To cut the rails, you'll need a hacksaw. A vise is handy for holding the rails while they are being cut. Any burred edges should be smoothed with a file so connectors insert easily. Railings are usually installed 31 in. high and even with the tops of the new posts.

MAKE A ROUGH SKETCH of your stoop with measurements as shown at the right. To find the number of 4 or 6-ft. rail sections you'll need, measure from the house to the edge of the platform. To determine whether a 4 or 6-ft. rail section is needed for the steps, measure the length of the stairs, top to bottom as shown. To find the number of newel posts required, figure one for each corner of the platform and one each for the top and bottom of the stairs. If railings consist of more than one section, add one post for each added section.

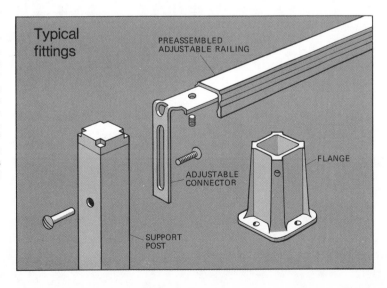

Typical fittings

PREASSEMBLED ADJUSTABLE RAILING

FLANGE

ADJUSTABLE CONNECTOR

SUPPORT POST

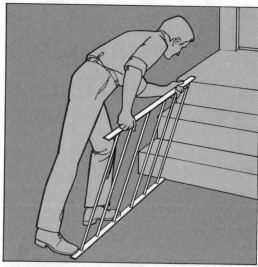

RAIL SECTIONS are attached to newel posts with adjustable connectors that require no drilling. Each connector slides inside the upper and lower rails and is tightened by a setscrew. Rail sections come in 4 and 6-ft. lengths and require support posts between sections. The same connectors attach the sections to the house. Before drilling holes, be sure to level the railing. If it's to be attached to wood, use regular screws; if to masonry, bolts in expansion anchors.

PREASSEMBLED RAIL SECTIONS adjust to any stair slope. To bend, put foot on the lower rail and push forward on the top rail to suit the stair pitch. Spindles are generally electrically fused to top and bottom rails to make the railing stronger than welded ironwork. Connectors are bent to the same angles as the rail section to join the section to the top and bottom newel posts. Extra wrought-iron scrolls, called lamb's tongue and finial, are available for the bottom newel post.

ONLY FOUR basic parts are required to add a wrought-iron railing to any porch or stoop—rail section, support post, adjustable connector and flange. Support (newel) posts are 1¼ in. square, 35 and 48 in. high. Posts fit into flanges, which are attached with setscrews; flanges are anchored to wood or masonry with screws or expansion bolts. Adjustable connectors join rail sections to posts like an Erector set. Complete railings are made up of 4 and 6-ft. sections, joined end to end with a post between.

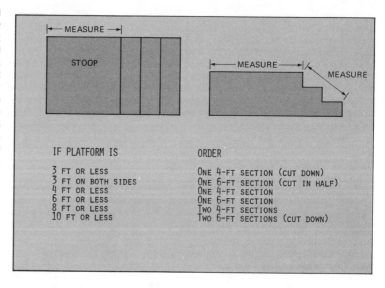

IF PLATFORM IS	ORDER
3 FT OR LESS	ONE 4-FT SECTION (CUT DOWN)
3 FT ON BOTH SIDES	ONE 6-FT SECTION (CUT IN HALF)
4 FT OR LESS	ONE 4-FT SECTION
6 FT OR LESS	ONE 6-FT SECTION
8 FT OR LESS	TWO 4-FT SECTIONS
10 FT OR LESS	TWO 6-FT SECTIONS (CUT DOWN)

Camping expert fits out an RV

■ PLAN AHEAD, and you can fit out your recreational vehicle for almost any activity—or a dozen of them. Take advantage of unused space, and you'll be able to stow the essential gear for boating, fishing, hunting, photography and hiking. The assortment of gear that fits in an economy-size rig, shown here, is as much as—or more than—held by highway rigs twice its size.

Shipshape and secure storage is the secret. The first shakedown cruise with this rig showed that the 11 cabinet doors offered easy access to the overhead compartments for stowing groceries and other small items. After a day on the move, however, nothing remained where it had been placed.

The first remedy was to install ¼-in. plywood partitions to divide the spaces in each compartment and assure a permanent berth for everything. Dishes are now safely held in cushioned racks designed for RVs. Glasses ride on other racks attached to the inner sides of the cabinet doors.

Opposite the dinette and behind the combination bunk/seat, an 18 x 36-in. oak table (a discarded dresser top) fits nearly atop a single folding leg. It's an ideal accessory worktable, does double duty serving guests in for dinner and has become so indispensable that it is left permanently in place. On the underside of the table, a shallow partitioned tray provides a handy place for innumerable small objects. Behind, on the wall, are two magazine racks.

Items originally stowed inside the two dinette seats were invariably lost in a jumbled hodgepodge. Two new plywood partitions created three compartments in one.

Beneath the other dinette seat is a complete hobby darkroom. The rather delicate enlarger head is cradled in plastic foam. One corner is reserved for photographic chemicals, all carried in unbreakable plastic bottles.

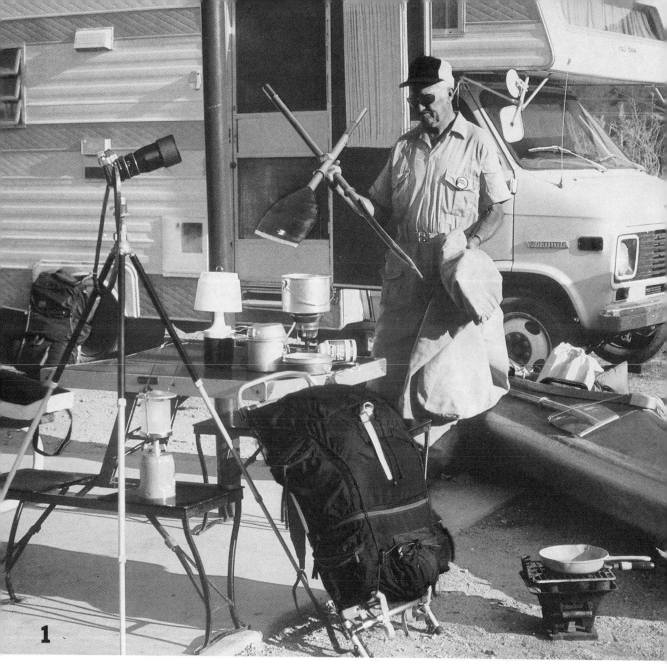

1

2

3

1 All the equipment above fits neatly aboard and out of sight in special ship-shape shelves and cabinets.

2 Photography can be a moneymaking hobby. Complete darkroom equipment fits safely under one dinette seat.

3 Top of an old dresser is a small table for typing travel stories; it stays permanently in place.

4 Envy of other campers is galley tool-board that holds short-order utensils in place with shock cords.

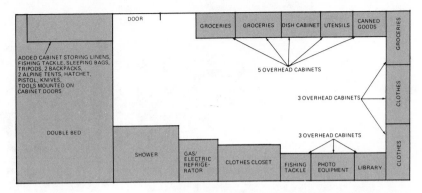

Overhead cabinets with added partitions and shock-cord tie-downs stow gear securely.

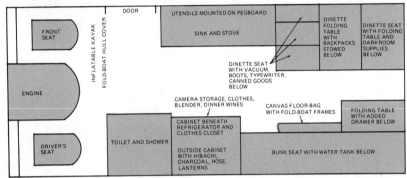

Undercounter bins plus compartments below dinette and bunk seats hold supplies.

For outdoor eating and activities there is a small 15 x 33-in. unit that unfolds from 4 in. thick into a table with four attached seats.

A surprising amount of usable space was retrieved by fitting a simple 44 x 28 x 10-in. cabinet into wasted space below the refrigerator and clothes closet. Provided with shelves and sliding doors, it's just right for storage.

To make RV cooking easier, all short-order essentials are stored on an enameled perforated board on the wall behind the sink and stove area. Utensils and accessories are held in place while the RV is on the move with elastic shock cords, available at camping supply outlets.

If you don't need the extra-long bed that comes with some cab-over mini-motor homes, you can use an electric carving knife to make quick work of slicing 14 in. from one end of its foam mattress. You will still have a full-size double bed plus room for yet another cabinet.

Equipment in the outside storage cabinet always seems difficult to find. Install a shelf and one dividing partition to make everything easier to reach.

Though this rig's roof deck permits toting a 17-ft. folding kayak topside, it is usually carried inside the vehicle. A slim, lightweight bag containing the kayak frame rides on the floor beside the bunk seat at the rear. A bag with the folded hull stands inside the door without blocking the entrance. An inflatable kayak lashed to the rear of the right front seat is out of the way.

Ingenuity rather than cost often determines the ways you can fit out your motor home or trailer for adventure.

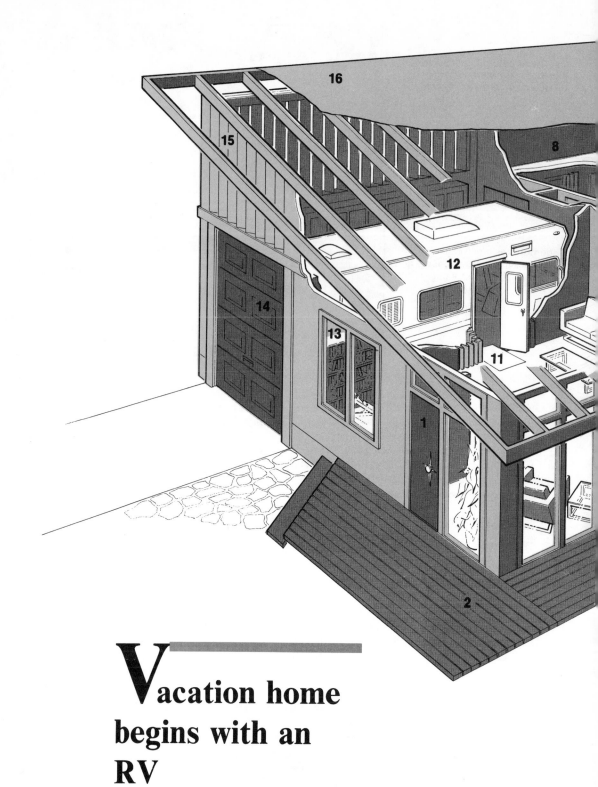

Vacation home begins with an RV

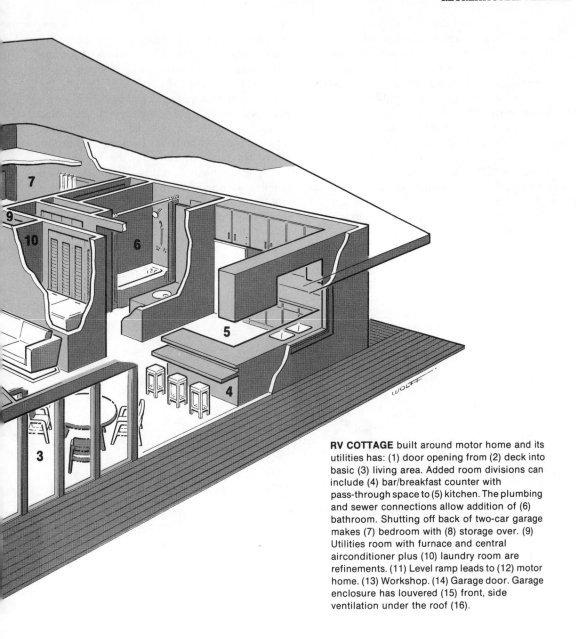

RV COTTAGE built around motor home and its utilities has: (1) door opening from (2) deck into basic (3) living area. Added room divisions can include (4) bar/breakfast counter with pass-through space to (5) kitchen. The plumbing and sewer connections allow addition of (6) bathroom. Shutting off back of two-car garage makes (7) bedroom with (8) storage over. (9) Utilities room with furnace and central airconditioner plus (10) laundry room are refinements. (11) Level ramp leads to (12) motor home. (13) Workshop. (14) Garage door. Garage enclosure has louvered (15) front, side ventilation under the roof (16).

■ A RECREATIONAL VEHICLE FAMILY in Toledo built a spacious one-room summer camp on its lakeside lot in Upper Michigan—and used its motor home parked alongside as bedroom, bathroom and kitchen. A fishing club in Maine, two mountain-climbing couples in Seattle, a family of six in Denver and a water-skiing group from Houston—all RV owners—are among many groups that have set up similar arrangements. So have several RV retirees in New Mexico.

One Winnipeg couple had more specific needs: "We were going to retire in two years," they wrote, "and had bought some land in central Florida. Like many undeveloped spots, it had no gas, electricity or water, but that was no problem since we could live in our motor home. Next to it we put up a simple one-room cottage in which we could store some of our things from our house up North, once we sold it. Eventually we expanded and fixed up the cottage to accommodate our children and grandchildren when they came to visit. Now, part of the year, we shut up the cottage and take to RV touring again.''

The shelter shown here was designed with the needs of such people in mind. The building starts with an enclosure and carport. Check local building codes and restrictions, plus insurance requirements, before getting started. Since some communities don't like the appearance of an RV, we have enclosed the carport with a garage door but louvered the top for ventilation so that the generator, airconditioner or furnace can be employed. For extensive use, exhaust hose extension or chimney connection may be installed.

The floor level of the camp cottage is planned at a height equal to the RV interior with a walkway leading in and accordion walls and ceiling fitting snugly around the RV door. Initially the room can be a simple screened-in shelter—with windows, walls, plumbing, room divisions, kitchen and bath, furnace and airconditioning, separate bedroom and outer decking added later. Storm shutters can close up the house completely when the owners drive off on tour. With sleeping accommodations in the vehicle and a fold-out sofa in the living area, back-bedroom space may be kept as a garage extension for a second car.

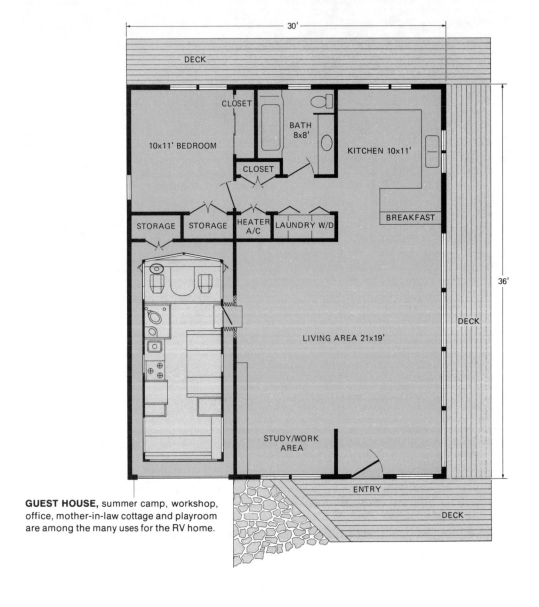

GUEST HOUSE, summer camp, workshop, office, mother-in-law cottage and playroom are among the many uses for the RV home.

Winterize your camper

ON MANY travel trailers utilizing a full underbelly, the only place stabilizer jacks should be set is under the words "Jack Pad," stenciled on the coach. These words indicate the location of the frame channels.

■ IN ONE WINTER your recreation vehicle can be ruined if you're not careful. That's right—improper winter storage can give your RV a down-at-the-heels look before spring.

The first important decision you must make is where to store your rig. This can make all the difference.

Above all, don't park it under a tree. Falling limbs can puncture the roof. Bird droppings can stain the exterior. Tree sap can be the devil to remove.

Avoid locations with heavy pedestrian or vehicle traffic, such as gateways, pathways, busy parking lots. The less the traffic, the less the damage to your RV. Also, watch out for spots where gates can swing open and strike the coach. In a storm, a wildly-swinging gate can severely damage the aluminum skin. It's easily punctured but hard to repair.

The best parking-storage locations are in wind-protected spots, or under a carport or roof of some kind. Many owners prefer to cover their coaches with a tarpaulin. Aluminum does not rust but eventually it begins to pit and corrode. Once the finish is dulled by weather, it takes a cleaning with acid to bring back the gloss.

Stabilizing the vehicle

Next, stabilize your RV properly. If the coach can be parked on a paved surface, that's best. Otherwise, set wood blocks underneath the stabilizer jacks. All four corners of the coach should be stabilized so that wind-action won't rock it about. *Caution!* Some travel trailers have locations plainly labeled "jack pads." Use stabilizer jacks *only* at those points. On any trailer, place stabilizer jacks under main frame members. *Never* place jacks under outboard struts or wooden channels.

Now, pay attention to your tires. Much misinformation surrounds the proper storage of tires. Latest research indicates that wherever industrial air pollution (smog) is a problem, tires should be elevated off the ground and deflated to 10 p.s.i. *Reason:* Deflating tires allows outer pores to close up. Inflating tires stretches the rubber and makes it more susceptible to damage. But remember, don't deflate tires that are carrying a heavy load. The best protection is to block up the axles with wood or concrete piers, deflate tires to 10 p.s.i., and cover tires with plywood or metal panels as protection against sunlight. This last step is extremely important in desert and Gulf Coast states, less critical in northern regions. Strong sunlight deteriorates tires rapidly.

Surest protection for tires during the winter is indoor storage. If you don't plan to use your vehicle during the winter months, jack up the chassis and remove the tires, deflate them and store them in a shaded, well-ventilated area.

With the RV anchored, you can tackle the interior. Coach interiors collect stale odors during idle storage. Causes can be traced to such things as leftover fish bait, a forgotten cheese

VACUUM ALL interior screens before storage. Dust on screens collects moisture which encourages rust. Also vacuum the cabinets, closets and drawers.

DRAIN, FLUSH and cleanse water tank so that all stale water tastes are removed. Keep the tank lid tightly closed during storage to keep out dust.

sandwich in a hunting jacket, or a spilled puddle of gasoline under a leaking portable generator. Look throughout the coach for leftover foods and beverages, opening all drawers, cabinets, storage bins, closets, and appliances. Something innocent as a cabbage leaf is potent when trapped in the airtight interior. With meticulous care remove soiled handkerchiefs, hunting boots and all dirty clothing. This will eliminate the source of many stale or sour odors.

Get those stains, too. Don't leave that streak of tomato juice on the dinette seat. Remove that tar stain from the floor tiles by the front door. Food stains on the table, cushions or bedding will be three times harder to remove after winter storage.

Remember not to leave metal objects in the sink or lying on the drainboard; even stainless steel can leave trace stains due to condensation of moisture inside a tightly closed coach. Vacuum all screens and the interior of all cabinets, closets and bins. Clean and wax the floor and all appliances. When you're sure that the interior is clean and fresh-smelling, then—and only then—start buttoning it up.

Now, shut off the LP-gas supply *at the tank*. On a trailer, that will be on the front frame. Twist the shutoff handle *clockwise* until it has seated firmly.

Enter the coach and be sure all appliance controls are set to the off position. Remove range burners and vacuum dust from the orifices. Replace burners and close the range cover to block dust. If the range lacks a cover, wrap burners in aluminum foil to prevent rusting.

Next, work on the plumbing. Because it can freeze, the plumbing system is particularly vulnerable. To prevent ice damage or bad taste next spring, follow these instructions:

1. Drain the water heater.

2. Drain the water tank and flush it for at least 20 minutes with clean water. Close the drain valve. Add half a box of baking soda and five gallons of water and let it stand overnight. Then drain the tank and flush it one last time. This action neutralizes unpleasant odors or bad taste.

3. Drain the sanitary holding tank, preferably at a service station outlet. Flush it thoroughly. Tighten the valve, and add a small amount of deodorant chemical to the tank. Where neces-

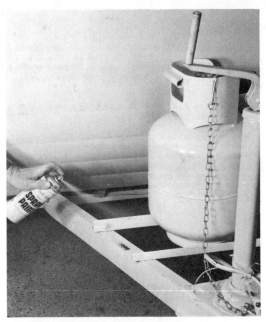

SIMPLE TOUCH-UP with spray paint over rust spots on the frame will prevent worse damage during storage.

sary, use air pressure to rid the sink trap, shower trap and internal plumbing lines of water. If overlooked, as frequently happens, these areas may freeze and break. Flush the toilet several times to rid lines of water.

4. Use a cup and sponge to drain the last bit out of the toilet commode. One coach manufacturer reports this item tops the list of frost-damaged hardware.

REMOVE GENERATOR and service gas engine to avoid leaks which may cause unpleasant odors and stains.

5. Place a cupful of antifreeze in each of the drain traps: shower, sink, tub, toilet and commode.

Just to make *sure* that all the water is out of the lines, raise the lift jack on the front of the trailer all the way, then lower it all the way down. This tilts the frame enough to drain stubborn pockets of water. On truck mounts and motor homes, you can accomplish the same thing by parking on a severe angle for a few minutes with all drains open.

Place aluminum foil between glass and screens to keep the sun from fading interior fabrics on cushions, gaucho beds and mattress covers. It's best to remove all bedding and blankets from the coach and store them in your home. But if you must leave bedding in the coach, cover it with plastic *loosely* laid over the fabric. This precaution will prevent wet spots and mildew stains in the event of a leak or draft which may let rain enter the coach.

One common mistake beginners make is to cork up the coach like a wine bottle. Don't do it! Proper *ventilation* is necessary even in the coldest climates. Condensation will become a problem in a closed, cold coach. Roof vents should be tightly closed, but one window or sidevent can be left open about one-half inch on the wind-protected side of the coach. Take the extra precaution of taping a plastic cover underneath the vent window inside the coach. In a severe climate where prolonged subfreezing temperatures are the rule it may be necessary to close

DEFLATE THE tires and store them indoors. Locate the jack under the frame rail, not an outboard strut.

Winterizing Special Gear

Some recreational vehicles are equipped with air compressor-type water-pressure systems. Turn the air compressor switch to OFF. Disconnect inlet and outlet hoses from pump and *rotate the pump manually* to expel water trapped inside.

Remove the 12-volt storage battery from the coach. Get it recharged to peak strength, then replace it. Do *not* reconnect battery cables to terminals. Spray a little anticorrosion coating onto the terminals and cable-heads. In extremely cold climates store the storage battery where it cannot freeze.

Don't forget the *water purifier!* They're popular these days. Remove the cover plate and make sure all water is out of it. (In the spring, replace the inexpensive filter cartridge with a new unit.)

Load-equalizer hitches should be removed and stored inside the storage bin or in your garage. The spring bars should get a light coat of spray paint. Bearing-ends of hitchspring bars should be lightly coated with bearing-grease and wrapped in foil.

Clamp-on side-view mirrors on the towing vehicle can be removed and stored for the winter.

If you have a portable electric power generator, it should be winterized. Drain the fuel tank. Drain and change the oil. Clean and replace the air-filter. If the unit is bolted inside the coach, just keep it covered. Otherwise, remove the generator and store it inside your garage. Set it on wood blocks, not on the bare floor. Wrap the generator with a plastic bag but do it loosely to provide for ventilation.

---

vents and windows securely. In this case, the coach should be opened every time a brief sunny period comes along.

Now, observe the following tips for specific types of recreational vehicles:

• *Travel trailers.* Spray a light oil onto the spring leaves. Lube zerc fittings on spring-shackles. Pull a plastic bag over the front coupler handle and tie it down (keeps coupler from rusting). Clean and repack wheel bearings on the chassis.

• *Pickup camper coaches.* If the coach will not be used during winter months, remove it from the truck with loader jacks. (You can rent loader jacks from many equipment yards or local coach dealers.) Loosen hold-down bolts or turnbuckles. Set coach down on wood blocks, *never* directly on ground. While the coach is off the truck, inspect its exposed underbelly for signs of splitting or swelling. Coat exposed areas with heavy mastic or weather-sealing paint recommended by local coach dealers. (Some sealers become sticky in hot weather.)

• *Motor homes.* All self-propelled recreational vehicles should be given a complete chassis-lube before storage. Engine maintenance should include oil change, oil-filter change, air-filter cleaning or replacing, and so on. Any service performed on your family car should also be performed on the motor home or van camper. Follow the same advice on tires: block up, deflate. If vehicle might be used occasionally during the winter, do *not* deflate tires, but rotate them at least once or twice each month to avoid flat-spotting.

• *Tent-trailers.* Clean fabric tops thoroughly *before storage.* Do not fold down a wet top. Dry it out first. Remove stains from fabric sidewalls or tops immediately. Keep the unit locked.

Despite all these precautions it's a mistake to ignore the recreational vehicle during the winter. At least once a week, walk around it and make a quick visual inspection. After every storm, enter the coach and look for signs of leakage or puncture-damage to roof. Don't let anyone lean objects such as bicycles, chairs or garden tools against the coach during the winter. In time, such treatment will dimple or dent the aluminum.

Using these winter-storage tips will save you time, money and trouble when you hit the road in the spring.

SEVERE FLAT-SPOTTING and rusted hub caps may result when you leave tires on trailer during the winter.

Improve your recreational vehicle

ADD BUILT-IN JACKS to your camper; then you can unload the coach anywhere.

■ LET'S SUPPOSE you have had your camper, trailer, van or motor home a couple of years and it's still in great shape. Maybe you don't want to trade, but you've got the itch to do something to improve it. Perhaps you have already purchased about every available option, including a portable generator and an airconditioner. What then?

Cheer up! Here are 15 ways to spruce up any recreational vehicle to increase convenience, extend its free range, sharpen performance, and in general make it a better traveling vacation home.

● *Bigger tires.* The first step should be to examine the rubber. Check the tire size and rating. Have your RV dealer tell you what is the widest tire your particular model can handle. For example, hundreds of thousands of pickups are still being sold with 7.50x16 tires, or with the smallest flotation units in size 8.00x16.5. Take a giant step toward improved stability by switching to the 9.50x16.5 or 10x16.5 supersingle, duplex-type tires. You'll need new wheels, of course, to go with them. Make sure you buy brand-name drop-center wheels for supersingle tires. Cheap imitations on the market sell for as low as *one-third* the price of specially-made flotation tire wheels. Cheap wheels negate the value of big tires; they're dangerous.

Many motor home owners can use the larger 12x16.5 tires. Wide tires increase traction, improve flotation and make a great difference in highway stability.

● *More water.* Most standard water tanks range from 15 to 20 gallons, occasionally to 30 gallons. An average family uses 5 to 8 gallons of water daily while vacationing, including water for drinking, cooking, bathing and sanitary flushing. Figure it out. At 5 gallons per day, a 20-gallon tank would last just four days. Increase your range away from water supplies the easy way. Install an *extra* water tank under a bed, or inside a closet or storage bin. Place it on the floor and near the axle to minimize the effect of extra weight. A 50-gallon tank in your trailer can more than double your free time afield.

● *Larger holding tank.* Your sanitary system is pretty well locked into the limits of the holding tank capacity. Fifty gallons of water cannot be held in a 22-gallon holding tank. Since space under the coach frame is limited, replacement of the existing tank is best. Holding tanks up to 50 gallons in size are available.

● *Another butane-propane bottle.* Though many persons refer to LP-gas containers as "tanks," the trade calls them *bottles*. One 5-gallon gas bottle will hold enough fuel to fire a three-burner range and a gas lamp for about five to six weeks of three-meals-a-day usage. But when the same 5-gallon bottle is used to fire a gas refrigerator, space heater and water heater consumption will zoom to five or six *days* per 5-gallon bottle. What a difference! There are a couple of practical alternatives. You can replace

EXTEND YOUR REAR BUMPER and add a trunk that will provide you with space for lots of spare gear.

BUY A HOLLOW BUMPER for your motor home or trailer in which to store easy-to-reach sewer hoses.

INSULATE WATER LINES and holding tank with foam or fiberglass to avoid freezing during winter camping.

REPLACE THE MANUAL water pump in an older coach with a modern 12-volt electric pump in a few hours.

INSTALL A NEW sway-control device; load-equalizer hitch or trailer dolly alone can't eliminate sway.

the existing 5-gallon bottle with a 7-gallon size. (Most storage bins have a little extra bottle size.) Or add an *extra* 5-gallon or 7-gallon gas bottle and double your fuel range afield. It's comforting to know your fuel capacity can outlast a five-day snowstorm.

• *Better heating.* Thousands of standard coaches without space heaters have been sold. Suffer no longer. You can get a small space heater that fits into unused closet or floor space, is modestly priced and very efficient. You can even get one for your tent trailer.

• *Instant water heater.* Did you know you can obtain a flash heater for your coach water system? For somewhere around a hundred bucks, you can find one that lets you wash in warm water, or run a cupful for coffee or tea just by turning a tap. It's instantly ready. This compact unit hangs on the wall like a decorator item. If you're an inveterate hot-drink camper, here's how to eliminate midnight pumping, firing up the range, or running a hot-water heater all night just to have a little hot water on cold mornings.

• *Added storage space.* If your coach seemed a bit overstuffed on your last vacation, you need more storage space. You can cut through the *outside wall* into a closet or under the bed area with a sabre saw. Ready-made bin-doors complete with piano hinge are available at low prices. See your coach repair shop or local trailer dealer. An outside-access storage bin is extremely handy for muddy boots, wet clothing, fishing creels, upland

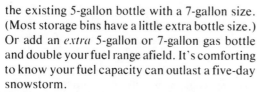

SWITCH the exhaust pipe from single to a twin system to increase performance and reduce the heat load.

BE SURE wheels can take big tires before you switch to them. The wheel shown is for a 12 x 16.5 tire.

A FOLDING TRAILER DOLLY tilts out of the way for travel but provides good support at the site.

SUPERWIDE TIRES double the foot print and provide improved stability, flotation and more traction.

game and other items that would be unpleasant inside the coach.

Even in the limited enclosure of a camper coach, you can box-in those wall-to-ceiling corners and add extra wall shelves very easily. Do the same in the cab-over bed section. Wherever you find unused wall space, add a shelf. On motor homes and trailers you can add a backwall trunk. Simply build a wood or metal framework, attach it to the rear wall and cover it with matching metal.

• *Built-in camper jacks.* If you own a pickup camper, you'll increase the convenience of your equipment if you install a set of built-in loading jacks. With them, you can remove the coach from the camper, save considerable fuel, and free the truck for other duty. Sometimes it's desirable to unload the coach at a campground to free the pickup for hunting and fishing side trips.

• *Eliminate swaying.* A load-equalizer doesn't automatically stop fishtailing. An equalizer hitch is designed to distribute heavy tongue loads to car and trailer areas better able to handle it. To eliminate swaying you need a sway-control device. This consists of a sliding arm restrained by friction-pads. Tension on the pads is adjustable to provide a dampening action at the exact level you need. For light loads, all you need is light tension to prevent feedback and whipping. There is also a sway control that operates hydraulically. Test a sway-control device with your load-equalizer to learn the difference.

• *Check trailer attitude.* Hitch up your trailer with a normal vacation load and full water tank, and park it on a level pad. Step back 50 feet and drop down on one knee. Study the trailer. Are the trailer and car frames riding level-horizontal? A trailer tongue high or low in front will not tow smoothly. It'll whip and sway easily, bottom over chuckholes and drag its tail in the street. If tongue is high, reduce tension on hitch spring bars. If it's low, increase tension. It may be necessary to move the hitch-head up or down, or to increase or reduce length of the hitch-ball shank to attain that level ride.

• *Pressurize the water system.* Does your older model have a hand-pumped water supply? Install a modestly-priced 12-volt water pump. Then your coach water system will operate at the turn of a faucet. Battery drain is low, convenience of the tap-ready water supply is great. Among other kinds of pressure systems are compact air compressors.

• *Replace thin mattresses!* In the early days of coach-building, many 2-inch mattresses were provided for standard models. Even today, you'll find a few in overhead bunks, though most are 4 inches thick. Most any RV dealer can obtain a 5 or 6-inch mattress on order. Thicker mattresses provide both extra warmth and comfort.

• *Add an overhead bunk*—maybe two of them, to handle the extra guests your children chronically invite along. Simple hangerbrackets screw to the wall for pipe-support hammocks. Or install sliding-type bunks which pull out for sleeping, push back to the wall to eliminate overhead restrictions.

• *Get heavy-duty shocks.* Years of road-testing recreational vehicles convinces most people that standard shock absorbers on a motor home, pickup, or sedan rarely are any good after 10,000 miles. On some models, shocks succumb at 5000 miles. In any case, heavy-duty shock absorbers will greatly improve performance, stability and tracking ability. They prevent wheel-hop; help keep your vehicle in a straight line. They minimize tire wear, too, and keep them in balance longer. On some test models, the difference in general stability after switching to heavy-duty shocks was positively amazing.

Replace chemical toilet with a new recirculating model with greater capacity *without* adding a holding tank. A space about 2 by 2 feet is enough for the recirculating toilet.

REPLACE the thin mattresses that came with your RV with 5 or 6-inch foam slabs and cover them yourself.

SABRE-SAW an opening, add flanges and a bin door from a trailer supply to make a storage box.

DOUBLE YOUR LP-GAS SUPPLY by adding a second gas bottle and installing a switch-over valve connection.

Tent trailer you can build

■ CAMPING IN A TENT TRAILER may well be the best and least expensive way to take vacations. Here's one you can build yourself.

Start with the chassis

To start, you need the trailer chassis. You can get this from a number of commercial metal works. Better still, you can scavenge it from an old beat-up trailer. Or you can build it from scratch, but you will need metalworking equipment and skills.

Should you want to build the chassis, the materials you'll need include two 10½-ft. sections of 2½-in. pipe. The trailer bed is 8 ft. long, but you'll need an additional 2½ ft. of length for the trailer tongue. Next, you need six 6½-ft. pieces of angle-iron stringers. These must be welded to the piping. Suspension springs, brackets, axle and wheels come next (see diagram). Positioning of the axle is critical. You want the completed trailer to tow straight behind the car, and be so balanced that only 50 to 60 lbs. of weight rest on the hitch. The trailer tires should be 4.80/4.00 x 8-in., which are rated to carry 1200-lb. loads at 60 mph. You want to try to keep away from large tires that call for wheel wells in the camper box for clearance.

Building the trailer body

The trailer body is basically a box made of plywood with 2 x 4 lumber used as joists under the floor.

Building the trailer box is simple once the plywood and lumber are cut to size. The plywood sections are designed to use every bit of eight 4 x 8 sheets of plywood. This means you don't have extra bits and pieces left over after construction. It also means you will not have the expense of extra sheets of plywood.

The floor should be ⅝-in. plywood, while the trailer sides, top and cabinets can be ⅝-in. or ½-in. Once you've cut all your wood, start by laying floors on joists and drilling through floor, joist and angle iron. Bolt together securely. Remember, this trailer will get a lot of bouncing.

To finish the floor, it's a good idea to lay tile. Remember to arrange the tile so the joint between two plywood floor sheets is covered. Lay the tile before adding the cabinets. This avoids intricate tile cutting and assures a proper fit.

For the cabinets, use strips of 1 x 3-in. lumber as supports and lengths of 2 x 2-in. as structural supports in the corners and at the ends. Cabinet doors can be covered with vinyl to spruce up the trailer interior.

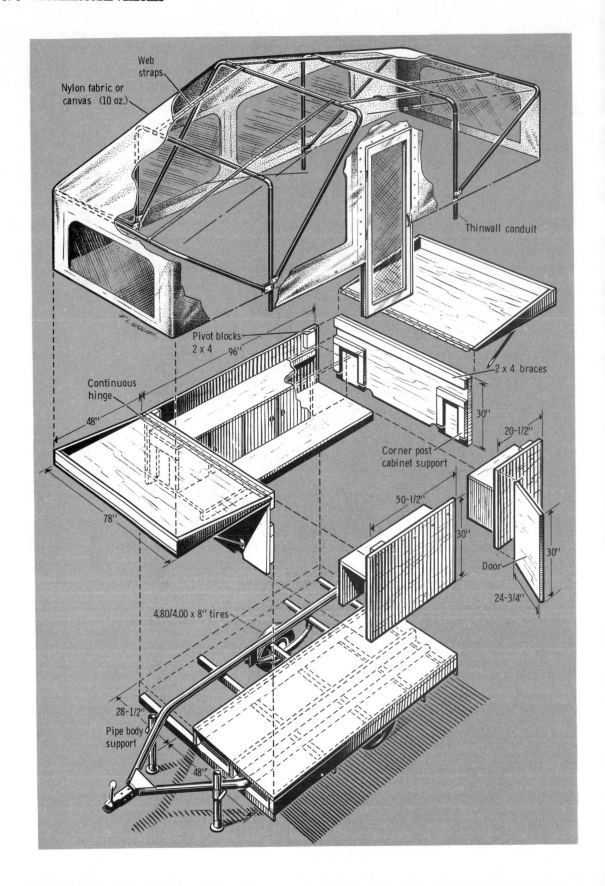

Web straps

Nylon fabric or canvas (10 oz.)

Thinwall conduit

Pivot blocks 2 x 4

96"

2 x 4 braces

Continuous hinge

48"

30"

20-1/2"

Corner post cabinet support

78"

50-1/2"

30"

30"

Door

24-3/4"

4.80/4.00 x 8" tires

28-1/2"

Pipe body support

48"

BUILD THE CHASSIS, then attach floor pieces. The trailer stands are attached to the forward portion.

FLOORING is laid on the joists. Attach floor and joists to angle iron with bolts or wood screws.

PREFABBING SIDES is a good idea. Note the position of the structural supports for cabinets.

For extra sleeping space, make the table so the support leg can be folded under and the table can be detached from the trailer bracket. Then lay the tabletop across the cabinet tops or benches. This can make up into another bed.

The tent canvas

It is possible that you may want some professional help with the tent canvas. Few people have sewing machines capable of double-stitch-

PLYWOOD PATTERNS

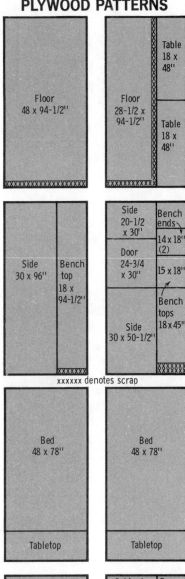

A SCREEN DOOR can be mounted. This door is removed and laid on the floor when you collapse the trailer.

PIVOT BLOCKS AND BOLTS are necessary for tent pole. Note steel straps that attach oblique pole.

ing 10-oz. canvas. Rig-binding and hand awls may also present a problem to the average do-it-yourselfer. A good awning and tentmaker can turn out a first-rate job for you when given the dimensions of your trailer. Remember, the tent poles, from pivot to peak, cannot be longer than the interior dimensions of the trailer box.

Electrician's thinwall conduit can be used for tent poles and ribs. This material can be bent with a plumber's bending tool. Or you can have formed corners of 13/16-in. bar inserted in saw-cut tubing ends. Wrap all joints with tape to prevent wear on the canvas. Web luggage straps can hold poles in the correct standing position.

Trailer building tips

• Remember to keep the door handle low enough so there is enough space for collapsed tent poles and canvas.

• Use heavy 2½-in. continuous piano-type hinges to secure bedwings to the trailer box.

• Use awning brackets as sockets for bedwing support rods.

• Use pivot blocks in corners so tent poles fall within the trailer box. Use pivot bolts to secure poles.

• Cement sponge-rubber weatherstripping around the top edge of the trailer box. When the trailer is closed in the travel position, this tripping will absorb shock and help keep road dust out.

• Paint the chassis so it will not rust and so it can be hosed off after long, muddy trips.

Remodeling

SOME MODERN materials, such as this vinyl flooring, will make any remodeling job easier and the final results more satisfying to the do-it-yourselfer.

■ REMODELING JOBS are nearly infinite in variety, and almost all are interesting. Some are quite hard work and require a lot of skill or great care, while others can be done easily by even the least skilled person.

What is remodeling?

Remodeling is different from renovation. Renovations are made to return a house to a particular design—to restore the character of its original construction. The concept of remodeling deals with changes that alter the basic character or fundamental design. In some jobs, you'll be interfering with the house's structural integrity in the process of making your changes. In others you'll be doing little more than replacing or covering a floor, adding wallpaper or painting. You may also choose to put an addition on to the house or to just rearrange traffic patterns indoors by moving a door.

The process of remodeling is one of suiting a house to your needs and tastes, while at the same time trying to remain at least within a reasonable distance of styles in your neighborhood. This point is often overlooked. When you expand a house and fancy it up past the point of other values in your neighborhood, the increased value of your home will not show up at marketing time. (It will, however, almost certainly show up at tax assessment time.) If you *need* a certain refinement, do it anyway, even though it is liable to cost more than it will add to the value of your home. If you simply *want* a space designed a certain way, and the cost is out of line with increased value, give careful consideration to the total costs of a remodeling job both now and when you sell.

Simple remodeling projects

Simple remodeling may consist of nothing more than installing new floor surfaces, ceiling surfaces, and wall coverings or paint. The overall improvement given by nothing more than a simple paint job is too often overlooked in the enthu-

siasm for ripping things out and replacing them with more expensive materials.

A good example is in old farmhouses, where the original plaster is in rough but solid shape. Too many people start right in ripping the plaster off the walls, readying it for drywall installation. In fact, if the walls are uninsulated or badly deteriorated, total removal down to the studs may be the only way to go. When there is decent insulation, one might consider such things as minor patchwork and top-quality wallpaper, or even texture paint that can then be easily sprayed on.

While a proper wallpapering job requires a sound surface, it does not require a perfect surface. You need to make only minor patches in holes and cracks. Texture painting requires virtually no wall patching on anything except major breaks in the wall. There is a great variety of textures you can use. Spray-painting texture paint will go much faster than using brushes and rollers. A good-quality airless spray gun shooting a tight spray pattern can be used for most paints, including heavy latex base paints, with little overspray problems.

Complex remodeling projects

In general, it is possible to go from minor, barely decorative changes in a home to making the place into a completely different type of building. Room additions, the changing of a ga-

THE AIRLESS sprayer in use here speeds both interior and exterior painting jobs and covers rough surfaces better than any other painting tool.

LAYING NEW hardwood floors used to be a tough job, requiring a great deal of skill, but new flooring installs in mastic over virtually any subfloor.

rage or porch into a room, the rearrangement of walls, the addition of new windows, doors, siding, roofing, fireplaces, room dividers, lighting, plumbing fixtures—each can add interest, excitement and drama to your house.

Changing traffic patterns is most often considered in remodeling. Here things are designed to give a sensible pattern to work areas so movement is consistent from a starting area to a finishing area, with good-size work spaces in each spot in between. Changing traffic patterns in the rest of a house may not be thought of in considering remodeling. Some house designs allow traffic flow interruptions of activities in major rooms or living areas. Often the cure is simply moving an interior door from one spot in a wall to another. This job is relatively simple, and provides an excellent reason to refurbish the rooms on both sides of the doorway. Exterior doors are a bit more difficult to move around with major remodeling because they usually open onto a stoop or porch of some kind. In these cases, quite a bit has to be relocated if you have to move the door farther than the width of the porch or stoop.

The greatest care is needed when you begin to move walls. Some walls are nonload-bearing. Taking these out, or changing their position, has little or no effect on the solidity of the house. Others, though, support other parts of the house. Their removal is critical, requiring a quite careful procedure of removal and replacement, or rebracing if the wall isn't to be replaced.

Remodeling help

The ideas in this section will give you a good deal of help in your remodeling project. You'll get other ideas by studying the catalogs of building product companies, or even by just walking through your home center store.

Manufacturers are designing new products that can be used more easily by those short on trade skills. Ceilings are easier to install. Sheet flooring has finally become relatively simple to lay. Ceramic tile is now designed to be installed more easily by the amateur. Wood flooring is easy to put in. Polyvinyl Chloride (PVC) plumbing products are simpler to install than copper.

Check the jobs needed to remodel your house, then carefully check products and prices you need to do the job. If you feel a project needs to be done but is too large or complex, call on a remodeling contractor. Just use as much care selecting a contractor as you would a doctor, and make sure, in states where licenses are required, that the contractor you select is licensed, bonded and insured.

Remodeling ideas

■ WHEN A DEEP BAY presents a drapery problem, a clever departure from common louvered shutters is to fit the window with four equal-size frames and cover them with matching drapery material. Colorful panels tie in beautifully with companion drapes. Hinged to fold like bifold doors, they fold back wide when full daylight is desired. The frames can be made from molding obtainable at your lumber yard. Just add hinges and knobs.

You (and other family drivers) will have no fear of pushing out the end of the garage should you sail in too fast some night if a wide step is formed in the floor at the time it is poured. Affording a safe, solid bumper for the front wheels, the wide step also provides a convenient walkway in front of the car, eliminating the nuisance of having to squeeze around it, front or back. A louvered step-to-ceiling closet centered in the end of the garage provides out-of-sight storage for tools, paints and children's toys.

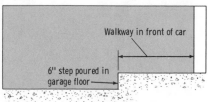

Walkway in front of car

6" step poured in garage floor

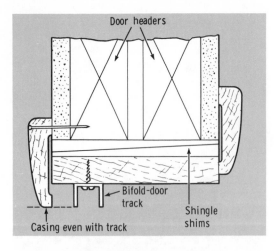

Requiring no more work than applying a casing around any door, this stunt for concealing the track of bifold doors is one that's applicable to both new construction and remodeling. As the sketch shows, it's simply a case of applying the top casing so it's even with the bottom edge of the track. Corners of the trim are mitered in the normal way but the side members are shortened. Nailing is limited to the edge of the casing. If you wish, a thin shim can be inserted in the cavity in the back of the top casing to also permit nailing into the frame header.

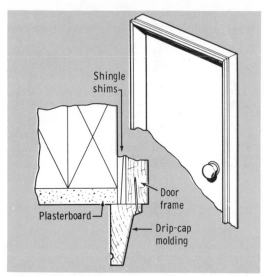

No reason why you always have to use customary flat casing around doors and windows. You can create a most interesting picture-frame effect by framing the door with common drip-cap molding. Decorative in itself, the molding produces a pleasing shadow effect, when mitered at the corners and applied taper-side in. The sketch shows how the molding is set back ¼ in. from the edge of the door frame and nailed on edge through its lip. Molding thickness will usually cover the gap between the frame and the wall. The idea is most practical when molding is applied to one side of the door, opposite the door's swing.

A highly functional bench for a modern entryway is this "masonry" one which offers storage for boots and other rain gear. Basically, it's a plywood box fitted with doors and covered with simulated sheet stone. A slab of cored latex rubber, fitted with a tailored cover, provides a comfortable cushion.

Fir plywood, ¾ in. thick, is used for the rough box which has a top but no back or bottom. A brace across the back at the bottom helps to reinforce the end. Typical cupboard-type lip doors are made to lap a frame in the opening and the edges of the stone. The stone treatment goes perfectly with a simulated slate-tile floor, such as the vinyl asbestos surface shown.

Tall panels of colorful fiberglass provide interesting "stained-glass" windows in this paneled wall facing an unattractive view. The windows blend with the vertical paneling, and give a colorful glow to the formal atmosphere of the dining room.

. Actually, the fiberglass windows look so attractive you might consider using them even when you aren't trying to cover an undesirable view.

The 8-in.-wide rough openings (12 in. apart) were framed with 1⅛ x 6½-in. members to project ¼ in. beyond the interior and exterior paneling. A rabbet for the fiberglass was formed with ⅜ x 1-in. strips placed 3 in. in from the inside edge. A second strip was used to hold the glass in place. As shown above, the windows are as attractive from the outside as the inside.

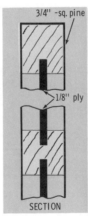

The graceful charm of a leaf-pattern grille can add a classic look to an austere foyer which features a plain glass panel. This one consists of five ready-cut wood scrolls grouped in a single mitered frame and held in the recessed window with four screws. The detail shows how the ¾-in.-sq. frame members are grooved down the middle to fit over the edges of the scroll-cut panels and form a frame.

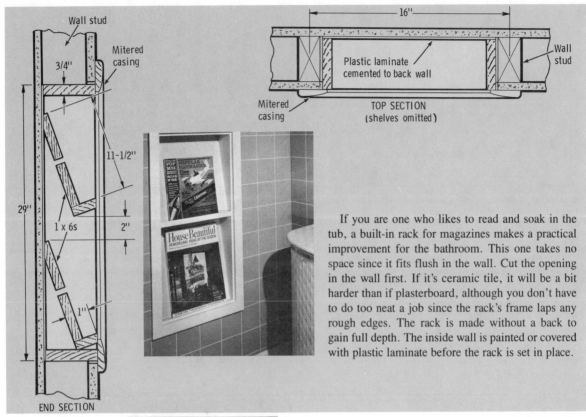

Wall stud

Mitered casing

3/4"

11-1/2"

29"

1 x 6s

2"

1"

END SECTION

16"

Plastic laminate cemented to back wall

Wall stud

Mitered casing

TOP SECTION
(shelves omitted)

If you are one who likes to read and soak in the tub, a built-in rack for magazines makes a practical improvement for the bathroom. This one takes no space since it fits flush in the wall. Cut the opening in the wall first. If it's ceramic tile, it will be a bit harder than if plasterboard, although you don't have to do too neat a job since the rack's frame laps any rough edges. The rack is made without a back to gain full depth. The inside wall is painted or covered with plastic laminate before the rack is set in place.

Pardon the pun, but a bathroom scale can get underfoot when standing around waiting for that once-a-day weigh-in. However, you can make a scale disappear in the wall and yet be Johnny-on-the-spot by attaching it to a swing-up door. First, pick a spot between two studs and cut a hole that's ½-in. smaller on three sides than the door. Then hinge the door to the floor so it swings flat against the wall and laps the opening. Finally, the baseboard is cut back for a mitered casing which frames the door. A magnetic catch holds the door shut, and a finger hole lets you give a tug to open it. How you attach the scale to the plywood door depends upon the type of scale.

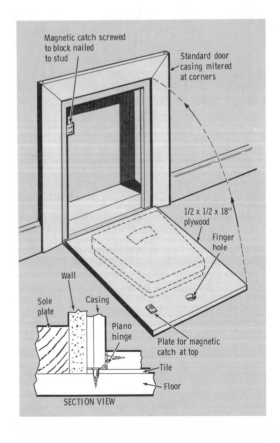

Magnetic catch screwed to block nailed to stud

Standard door casing mitered at corners

1/2 x 1/2 x 18" plywood

Finger hole

Wall

Sole plate

Casing

Piano hinge

Plate for magnetic catch at top

Tile

Floor

SECTION VIEW

If your bedroom is your only haven when your children invite the gang over for Saturday night, you won't feel so marooned with a get-away-from-it-all spot like this. Likewise, when the adults take over downstairs for an evening of bridge, it will serve the rest of the family as a comfortable out-of-the-way place to read, watch TV or do homework.

It's a great idea for putting a spare bedroom to good use, the main feature being a divider wall which earns its keep and then some. A his-and-hers affair, it's split down the center to provide a dressing table and mirror on one side and kneehole desk and shelves on the other. The big full-length mirror lets you look your best. It starts out as a T-shape wall with a 10-ft. soffit. Desk and vanity are built-in against a dividing wall.

The dimensions are not critical and will have to be adjusted to your floor plan. The version shown here was painted white with dark stripes around the drawers, mirror, etc. to provide contrast. Again, you can finish it to suit your decor.

We illuminated our version with standing floor lamps and lamps placed on the desk, but you could also place fluorescent bulbs in the top.

This built-in buffet cabinet lets you store table linens without creases. It takes only 11 in. of depth and hides behind sliding doors that masquerade as wall paneling. Camouflaged by a picture, the unit looks like an unbroken wall when the doors are closed.

Actually it's two cabinets in one, one side having adjustable shelves for china and crystal, plus two drawers for silverware; the other having rows of 1-in. poles for hanging 52-in.-wide table linens. With no creases or folds, the linens can be used immediately without a second pressing.

If you have plastered walls, you'd still create a second wall 11 in. out from the existing wall, frame a 10-ft. opening, then set the premade cabinet in it and add trim around three sides. The silverware drawers measure 10 x 22 x 9 in. and swing out for full access. Dowel pins in the front corners of the drawers pass through fixed shelves, above and below. Clearance is left at the sides so the drawers will swing without binding.

The best place to locate the cabinet is in the dining room near the table so that the silver, linens, china, and crystal will be at hand when you are entertaining. Whichever wall you choose, you will want to panel the wall to match the cabinet if it's not already paneled.

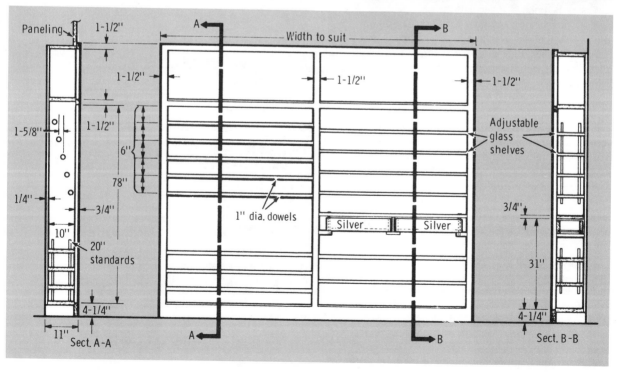

OUT OF SIGHT but not out of mind, there's an extra bed waiting for that unexpected overnight guest.

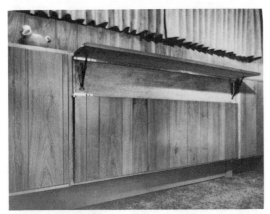

A SWING-UP PANEL, actually the bed's leg, is opened first and locked at a 90° angle by table-leaf brackets.

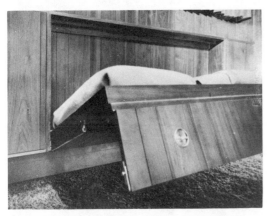

THE BED can be swung down when the bolts at the sides are unlocked. Seatbelts hold the mattress and bedding.

How are you fixed for an extra bed? Could you put up an unexpected guest for the night? This bed is stored out of sight for just such emergency use. It swings down like a Murphy bed and up again.

As you see in the photos at the left, the bed pivots flush in a shallow cabinet that's only 12 in. deep and which extends wall to wall. Flanking bedding-and-storage cabinets at each end of the bed add to its overall convenience. The resulting ledge across the top provides a welcome shelf area for books, bric-a-brac, toys and pictures.

The tray-like bed frame holds a standard 6-in.-thick foam-rubber mattress. This along with a double sheet, bedspread, blanket and pillow is strapped in place with regular car seatbelts to fold intact.

The original unit was installed in a small dressing room off a master bedroom paneled with prefinished plywood. The paneling shows though the open back when the bed is down and provides a finished look. Matching paneling was

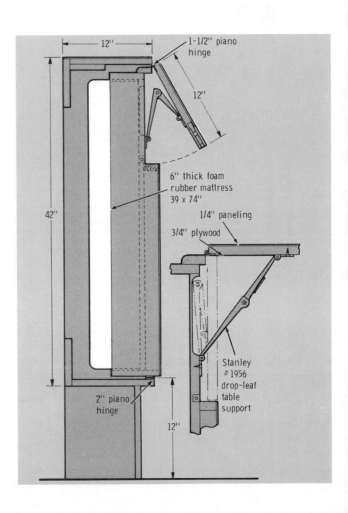

used on cabinet doors and underside of the bed to give the unit a built-in appearance.

Basically, the unit consists of three cabinets, all more or less built in place and supported by a single shelf board 12 in. off the floor. Top and bottom cleats, screwed securely to wall studs, hold all units firmly to the walls and floor.

In the drawing, note how the bed's hinged "leg" folds flush in a recess extending across the top. Clearance for the spring-loaded drop-leaf table supports which hold the leg at 90° is provided by routing wells in the bottom bed board. King-size piano hinges are used to hinge the leg as well as the bed. Sliding flush bolts lock the bed shut. Room for a bolt at each end of the leg is provided by making the latter an inch or so shorter than the bed. The mattress sits on a piece of ¾-in. particle board.

Finish the unit to match the walls. All exposed edges should be covered with wood tape to match the panelling. The cabinet doors on each end are held closed by hidden magnetic touch locks.

THE BED CABINET PROPER is anchored to wall and studs by driving screws through top and bottom cleats.

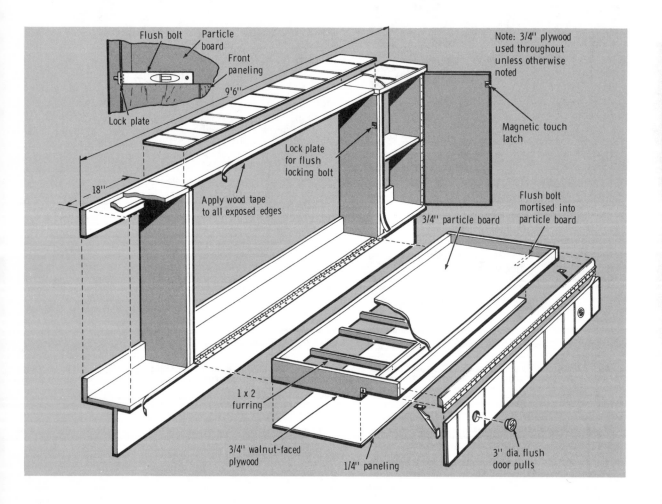

New home— without moving

SKETCH shows original porch that was enlarged to 16 by 30 feet to yield a family room and larger kitchen.

■ TODAY, ADDING TO or remodeling your home, rather than searching for a newer, larger house, is often the wiser choice for a homeowner. Depending upon size and selection of finishing materials, it is almost certain to be the less expensive approach.

Money isn't the only factor. Most of us like where we live, and if you have youngsters in school, a family shift will require more than a few adjustments.

Since the property that this family owned would permit them to build the room they needed, their decision was to stay put and add on. They also increased their living area by adding a lighted patio. And, since the original house was due for a reroofing, the entire house was covered with hand-split cedar shakes.

The vaulted ceiling is simply ½-in.-thick plasterboard over 2x6 collar beams. To finish, the plasterboard was heavily textured with paint and the joints covered with decorative oak beams.

For general use, the lighting concealed behind the wood soffit close to the ceiling gives sufficient illumination. It consists of fluorescent strips which reflect off the painted ceiling. For

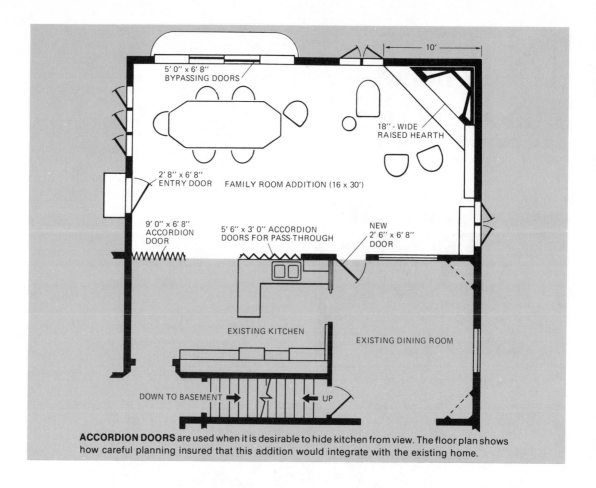

ACCORDION DOORS are used when it is desirable to hide kitchen from view. The floor plan shows how careful planning insured that this addition would integrate with the existing home.

decorative appeal, oak dentil molding was used around the room where walls and ceiling meet.

The original heating plant was capable of handling the new room; thus, it was not necessary to install new heating equipment. But the builder did relocate the thermostat, placing it in the new room. The single thermostat handles the entire house adequately from this location.

Desiring overall, even lighting, rather than one or two ceiling fixtures, the homeowner chose a luminous ceiling for the kitchen. Even here, the owner decided to "customize." The plastic, which comes in 2x4-ft. sheets, was halved to create 2x2-ft. sections. Installation was standard using the metal grid system. For visual tie-in with the family room, simulated beams were spaced at intervals across the ceiling.

The kitchen cabinets, custom-made, are also of oak. As seen in the photos and floor plan, strategically placed accordion doors can be kept open for general everyday use or closed when desired. They were placed at the peninsula counter so that area can be left open.

The brick-patterned vinyl flooring was picked up from the old kitchen and relaid.

To make the step platform by the sliding doors, slate was simply embedded in concrete. The concrete patio has a smooth steel-trowel finish and raked lines radiating from the platform. The outdoor lighting was solved by simply setting a plastic globe on steel pipe, which, of course, is erected in a footing.

What makes this addition particularly attractive is continuity of design, both indoors and out. It is obvious that the homeowner and builder worked closely together on the project and it shows in the finished product. The new hip roof ties in perfectly with the existing house roofline. And that is important. A poorly or hastily conceived addition will almost always result in a structure that has a tacked-on look. This is something to avoid if you want to add to, rather than detract from, the value of your home.

It might even pay to have an architect look at your home and make suggestions so that you will avoid this common pitfall.

CAREFULLY planned addition has bypassing doors located to give the best view of the outdoors. The fireplace is built of kasota stone and has an oak mantel.

ENLARGED KITCHEN features a luminous ceiling. Oak beams were added for a visual tie-in with the new room. The cabinets are also of oak with a suede finish, white laminate was used on the countertop.

Facelifting— cheapest way to get a new home

■ IF YOUR HOME is due for repainting, step back and take a long, hard look at it, then decide whether a paint job alone will give you the look you really want. Chances are the house, as well as its shrubbery, can stand some "pruning." Ornate but useless gingerbread and hardware can be removed, for example. In some cases removal of an "improvement" (something a former owner made that you probably wouldn't have) will restore the house to its original architectural concept—resulting in aesthetic improvement. And older homes will nearly always benefit by grading and landscaping that brings them visually closer to the ground.

Several such low-cost ways to update your home are described here. While your particular house may not be shown here, you'll find many ideas that will work for you.

Charm and value are added to this tract-type single-level dwelling, typical of the most economical homes to be built today. The simple design lends itself to easy, inexpensive improvement. Note how the colonial touches—windows, shutters, plants, and lamps—add charm. The garage extension lengthens and adds to the convenience and value of the home.

Restore true character to a roomy, two-story frame home with little more than careful selection of color and the removal of some "improvements" that violated the building's original character. Here, removing a wrought-iron rail and adding carriage-house-style fascia restores the balance and importance of the first floor.

Change for the better here amounts principally to relocation of the porch steps for better access to and from the driveway. Moving them eliminates the need for a front walk that divides the house down the middle. The clean, unbroken lines of the new porch give the facade better proportions and the house an improved overall appearance. Removing the overgrown bushes and replacing them with the low-profile plantings lets the new front show to advantage. If the upkeep of a porch that is glass enclosed doesn't pay off in well-used living space, consider a change that will simplify the maintenance and improve the general looks.

A change in grade can make the major difference. The good features of this house are all but lost in its height. To bring it down to earth, a retaining wall is added parallel to the sidewalk. The yard is then filled and landscaped to conceal the foundation. A colonial-style entry, new windows (note the special treatment of bathroom window above the entry), plus the addition of dormers, shutters and coordinated coach lights adds up to a rather ambitious remodeling job. But it all combines to reveal the house's true potential. If your home has a roofed niche, as shown at the top, it can be left as is or enclosed (sketch at right) for additional space.

Dramatic changes you can make yourself

■ THE DRAB-LOOKING HOUSE on the narrow lot in the photo below was originally built to serve as a lakeside summer home.

The house was full of problems, almost too many to solve. The living area was inadequate for the owners and their two growing boys. And the narrow parcel of ground ruled out any expansion into the side yards. Combined, the two levels had a scant 960 sq. ft. of living space. A complete front-to-rear remodeling changed the picture.

AS SHOWN in these before and after photos, the house underwent a dramatic transformation. You might not even suspect it is the same house.

THESE PICTURES of the kitchen and dining area show the pass-through connecting the two. Also shown are the contemporary-styled cabinets. These have been equipped with invisible latches for a more modern look.

The floor plan was opened to all kinds of possibilities, but things started to happen when the decision was made to move the stairs outside.

The first step was to build a new circular staircase in a round "tower." What had been a small deck in front of the living room was then enclosed to double its size. Twelve feet were added to the rear of the house and interior partitions were reshuffled.

With remodeling completed, the chalet-style boasts an impressive 1900 sq. ft. of living space laid out for a lot of living. It is chock-full of dramatic and sensible ideas. Some features can be duplicated easily; others require professional know-how. All are handsomely designed and installed with care. Whether you are a do-it-yourselfer or prefer to hire others to make renovations, you're almost certain to spot some ideas that seem made to order for your house.

As shown on the previous page, the dramatic change is obvious in the "after" shot of the completed remodeling. The tower, which houses the circular staircase, blends well with the chalet styling, and by breaking the severe slope of the roofline adds interest and pleasing balance. It creates the impression that the whole house is wider than the original building when in fact it is not. The tower windows are insulated units: they're designed to be heat-absorbing and glare-reducing.

The huge expanse of exposed roof was covered with attractive, handsplit cedar shakes. A wood preservative was applied, and the shingles were left to age naturally.

The existing roof line was continued over front and rear additions to integrate the design.

The new roof was planned with energy conservation in mind, too. A 6-ft. overhang was added to the length of the house on both sides to shield it from the summer sun, which would tax the air-conditioning system. But the design admits warming rays from the lower-angled winter sun to assist the heating plant.

The rough-sawn cedar siding enhances the natural beauty of the house's lakeside site.

Rather than hide the exterior doors with storm

THE NEW LIVING ROOM features beamed ceilings and lots of glass for an open look.

or screen doors, insulated steel doors were installed (which eliminate the need for either). Door exteriors were painted with epoxy enamel and the interiors were covered with a wood-grain pattern plastic laminate matching the interior oak trim.

The remodeled and enlarged kitchen has a false A-ceiling. Space created between it and the old ceiling is used to route wiring, pipes and ductwork. Gone is the bothersome stairway that had cramped the old kitchen. In the expanded area now appears an appliance and cabinet layout that would please the fussiest of chefs. The kitchen is flooded with light; eight recessed-can fixtures installed in the ceiling are angled to provide even, shadowless lighting.

The 6x6-in. ceiling beams are also false. Hollow and fashioned of red oak, they—like all interior trim—are finished with walnut oil stain. To minimize daily upkeep, kitchen walls are treated with a fabric wall covering that resists bumps, bangs and scrubbing. For underfoot comfort, the floor is finished with a commercial polyester carpeting.

If there is a single attention-getter in the kitchen it is the functional pass-through connecting kitchen and dining room. What used to be a doorway was closed at the bottom and neatly framed with trim. The countertop was built to create a 12-ft.-long ledge (not visible in the photo) on the dining room side for buffet-style entertaining.

Another reason for the opening was to allow better use from the dining-room area. With its stools, that side of the counter can be used for breakfast, lunch and snacks. The dining room wall seen opposite the pass-through is clad with ½-in. plywood (instead of plaster or plasterboard) and covered with wall fabric. The owners periodically change picture groupings—this wall lets them drive nails wherever they want without the need for patch jobs.

The living room was doubled in size when the additions were completed. The two walls facing the lake were opened up to let in the view—but not the heat.

The pair of "useless" fixed windows flanking the fireplace in the original living room were

THE TWO WINDOWS that used to flank the fireplace have been closed and replaced with a slit window at the right.

THE VANITY shown below was built by the owner to complement the matching drapes, ceilings and walls.

A SKYLIGHT above the shower is used to bring natural light into the bathroom as shown at left.

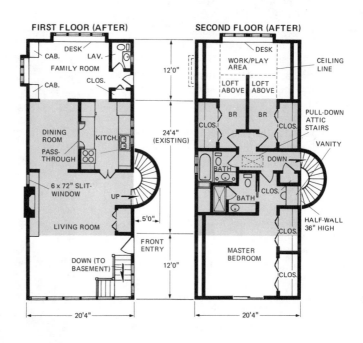

THE LILLIPUTIAN SIZE of the lot that this home occupies is appreciated when you know that the fence in the fore-ground separates the property from a neighbor's. The railing on the second level (false balcony) de-emphasizes the tall look and repeats the balcony detail on the house front. Generous use of wood decking creates an illusion of a larger house and lot. The view of the house from a distance shows how railroad-tie walls blend with the styling.

closed in, and a 6x72-in. slit window was in-stalled behind the mantel. Note that this window is the only opening on that sidewall. It creates a dramatic focal point as light streams in over the heavy mantel. The fireplace was enlarged and a massive, rough-hewn mantel added.

The shower in the bath added off the master bedroom has a skylight because this was the only way natural light could be brought into the room. The ceramic-tiled stall shower has a door that's framed in bronze metal to match the vanity mir-ror frame.

A new look for the old bathroom was created by using drapery that matches the walls and ceil-ing. The pattern shown is a cotton fabric.

The active pattern on the walls, ceiling and drapery underscored the need for a handsome vanity design that would hold its own. Built by the owner, its luxurious sculptured look was achieved through the use of standard lumber-yard moldings.

For structural reasons, the stair tower is erected on a concrete slab. Such a construction provides a solid base for anchoring circular stairs. Treads are cantilevered from the wall, thus eliminating the need for a post. Because of

this, the handrail runs around the inside perime-ter of the treads—rather than the outside—which is typical of factory-built circular stairs.

THE CIRCULAR STAIRS were precut in the shop, then assembled and welded at the job site.

Sliding doors and windows you can add

■ ROOMS that have ample windows usually seem bigger and more pleasant than under-lighted, closed-in rooms. Adding a new window or expanding an existing one is not a hard job. Start early on a fair day and you'll be done before supper.

For a more ambitious project (and a lot more light), try opening a room by installing sliding glass doors. More framing is required, but you can still plan it for a one-day job.

Modern windows and sliding glass doors come ready to install. Some have a flashing flange built into each unit. Nail it to the sheathing, cover it with siding and the exterior is finished—the wood, wrapped in vinyl, needs no painting.

Plan the opening

You already have at least one window in the room. Your wall is clean, solid and freshly painted. So you'd be crazy to cut a big hole in it, right? Wrong. Just make sure you cut the hole in the right place.

● Stay away from electrical outlets. Rewiring will add time and trouble to the project.

● Don't box yourself into a corner; stay away from the extra corner studs and leave room for trim.

● Try for an opening 1½ in. in from an existing stud. Add a jack stud and eliminate inside patching on one side.

● In general, select a unit that matches the style of those already on your house. Matching the sill height and grille pattern will make the window

SLIDING GLASS DOORS provide a quick way to enclose a porch. You need to frame the opening, but you eliminate insulation, sheathing, siding, wallboard, taping and painting. The doors shown are double-glazed.

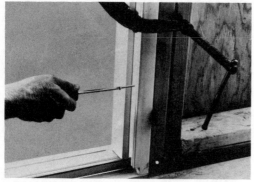

C-CLAMPS will draw the vinyl flashing against the sheathing. Shim between the frame and stud for a vertical alignment.

TREATED SILL SUPPORT is attached beneath the overhanging metal sill with 10d casing nails. You can also glue this joint for added strength.

STATIONARY door panel is installed first. Predrilled holes for fastening the brackets assure proper alignment of the panels with the frame.

METAL BRACKETS are screwed to the door and frame at the head and the sill. These brackets serve to lock the stationary panel in place.

FOLLOW ROUGH-OPENING dimensions supplied with your unit for framing. The weight load from a second story or roof rafters is transferred to the double studs at each end.

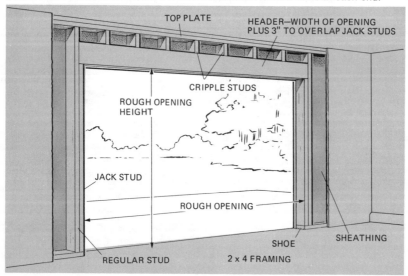

TOP PLATE

HEADER—WIDTH OF OPENING PLUS 3" TO OVERLAP JACK STUDS

CRIPPLE STUDS

ROUGH OPENING HEIGHT

JACK STUD

ROUGH OPENING

REGULAR STUD

SHOE

SHEATHING

2 x 4 FRAMING

ADJUSTABLE ROLLERS on the operating door ride on a rib in the sill. A vinyl thermal barrier runs the length of the sill to provide insulation.

A HEAD STOP screwed to the head jamb completes the installation of the track for the doors. Rollers can be adjusted to the proper height.

THE FINISH CASING is installed by nailing through sheathing into the studs with 10d casing nails.

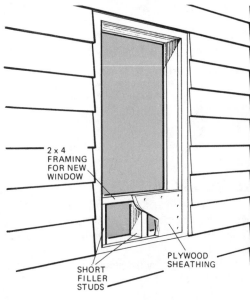

2 x 4 FRAMING FOR NEW WINDOW

SHORT FILLER STUDS

PLYWOOD SHEATHING

WINDOWS do eventually wear out. Rotting sills or a warped sash may be beyond repair.

REMOVE THE WINDOW. Add filler studs and sill to fit the new unit. The siding stays intact.

ADD SHEATHING over the new framing. Cover with tar paper and then lift the window into place.

TO REMODEL WITH A NEW WINDOW, follow these steps: First, pick a window in the style you want that's slightly smaller than the existing one. This way you add to the frame and leave the siding intact. Second, add filler studs, sill, sheathing and tarpaper. Third, install the new window, caulk and replace exterior siding. Fourth, add insulation and wallboard to the interior; tape, paint and add grille clips if desired.

look as if it grew there. This holds true for sliding glass doors.

Headers and sills

Any time you remove a stud you weaken the wall. Where the location of your window or door is not adjustable, you may even have to remove a critical load-bearing support.

Weight carried by the studs you take out must be transferred to double studs at each side of the opening with a header. On a moderate-sized window, two 2x4s spiked together will do. Nail header between the side studs; support each end with a jack stud. The space between these jack studs is the rough-opening width. Play it safe and increase the dimension required for your unit by ¼ in. This will give you room to shim for perfect alignment.

The header over a sliding glass door must be stronger to carry the weight of a second story wall and roof rafters. *Tip:* overbuild rather than skimp on material. In many new development houses cracks appear in the wall around openings. Insufficient headers above and beams below are often the cause.

To be safe, use double 2x6s for a 5-ft. slider, 2x8s for a 6-ft. unit, 2x10s for anything bigger. On three-panel sliders, use 2x12s. If weight from above causes your header to deflect (the engineering term for sag), your doors won't glide smoothly.

RIGID FLASHING flange is part of the window and is nailed through sheathing into studs. Siding removed from around the opening is recut and replaced.

REMOVE INTERIOR trim carefully. When adding a new window or replacing an old one, fill in with insulation and patch the interior wall before trimming.

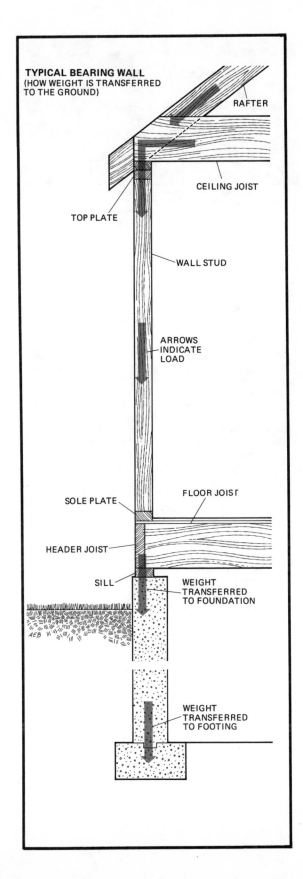

TYPICAL BEARING WALL
(HOW WEIGHT IS TRANSFERRED TO THE GROUND)

RAFTER

CEILING JOIST

TOP PLATE

WALL STUD

ARROWS INDICATE LOAD

SOLE PLATE

FLOOR JOIST

HEADER JOIST

SILL

WEIGHT TRANSFERRED TO FOUNDATION

WEIGHT TRANSFERRED TO FOOTING

Removing a bearing wall

■ OFTEN A MAJOR home-remodeling project requires the removal of an existing wall. The usual reasons are to create a one-room effect between dining and living rooms and to enlarge a room by knocking out the wall between it and an unused bedroom or garage. Often, however, wall removal is only partial: When redecorating plans call for installation of sliding doors, for instance, or making a wide-arched opening where a single door now exists.

If the wall to be removed is simply a partition wall—that is, nonload-bearing—the task is relatively simple. But if the wall supports weight from above (see drawing, left), it is a bearing wall. In this case, it's important that a proper-size header be installed over the new opening (span) to handle the load adequately from above—and its transfer to the foundation.

Though removing a large section of a bearing wall is a job usually best left to a pro, you will be well advised to have a working knowledge of just what this task involves. Most smaller jobs can be tackled with confidence by a knowledgeable home handyman; the information on these pages will help you do that. As can be seen in the drawings and text, the first big chore is to determine whether the wall is, in fact, a bearing wall. If it is, here's how you can remove it.

Removing the wall finish

Before starting to remove the surface of any wall, determine where all electrical, heating and plumbing lines run. If any are in the wall, do not use power tools near the area. Turn off power to all outlets in the wall and use a hammer to remove plaster or drywall from these sections. Also, protect the floor with a dropcloth. Better yet, use a canvas tarp over the dropcloth. Tape the floor covering along the edges which will be walked over, or debris kicked beneath will scratch the floor. For safety, stop periodically and haul accumulated debris outside. If this is left underfoot, it can cause accidents.

The best way to remove a drywall is with a sabre saw. Simply run its blade alongside studs to make vertical cuts, and make horizontal passes to create the

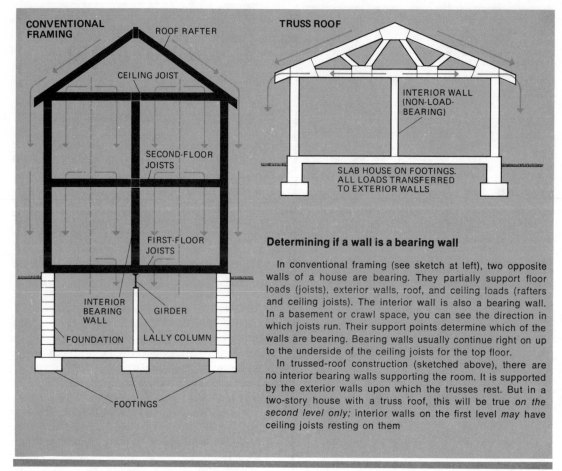

CONVENTIONAL FRAMING

ROOF RAFTER

CEILING JOIST

SECOND-FLOOR JOISTS

FIRST-FLOOR JOISTS

INTERIOR BEARING WALL

GIRDER

FOUNDATION

LALLY COLUMN

FOOTINGS

TRUSS ROOF

INTERIOR WALL (NON-LOAD-BEARING)

SLAB HOUSE ON FOOTINGS. ALL LOADS TRANSFERRED TO EXTERIOR WALLS

Determining if a wall is a bearing wall

In conventional framing (see sketch at left), two opposite walls of a house are bearing. They partially support floor loads (joists), exterior walls, roof, and ceiling loads (rafters and ceiling joists). The interior wall is also a bearing wall. In a basement or crawl space, you can see the direction in which joists run. Their support points determine which of the walls are bearing. Bearing walls usually continue right on up to the underside of the ceiling joists for the top floor.

In trussed-roof construction (sketched above), there are no interior bearing walls supporting the room. It is supported by the exterior walls upon which the trusses rest. But in a two-story house with a truss roof, this will be true *on the second level only;* interior walls on the first level *may* have ceiling joists resting on them

desired-size chunks. When all of the plasterboard is removed, clean the nails from all the studs you plan to save and reuse. If the studs are to be thrown out—rather foolish in these days of high lumber prices—drive home all nails before ripping out the studs.

Removing plaster and wood lath is a different—and dirtier—story. Besides protecting the floor, it's a good idea to drape dropcloths over doorways to keep white dust from spreading through the house. Open windows for ventilation and be sure to wear a face mask.

The handiest tool to have when removing a plaster wall is a bayonet-type power saw. A sabre saw does the job, too; it just takes a little longer. Use a plaster-cutting blade in either type of saw; an ordinary blade will soon become dulled and useless.

To start, make a plunge cut in one of the bays between studs and run the saw horizontally until you come to a stud. Then turn the saw in a vertical position, either up or down, and continue cutting. After you've made both horizontal cuts and one vertical cut, you can start the last vertical cut. Here you'll find that as the tool cuts into the wood lath behind the plaster, the lath chatters. Thus, it is best to have a helper hold a board against the wall on the outboard side of the saw to minimize lath chatter.

It's a good idea to give your power tool a thorough cleaning as soon as the job is completed. There will be considerable accumulation of white dust in the tool's air ports, and unless it is completely blown out, excessive heat can build up and burn out the tool.

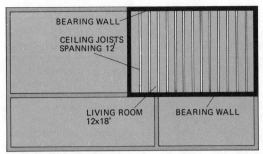

Slab-house bearing walls

In a slab house where visual inspection of the joists above is impossible, the easiest way to check which walls are bearing is by living-room dimension. If, for example, your living room measures 12x18 ft., ceiling joists will normally run the shortest dimension—12 ft. The bearing walls will be the 18-ft.-long walls. Also, it is often easy to spot the plasterboard nails in joists—by the rows of dark spots on the ceiling

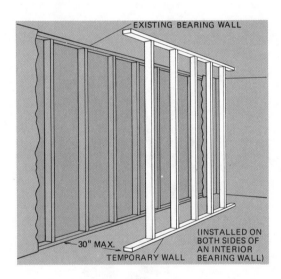

Temporarily supporting the load

Since a bearing wall denotes a wall which is supporting some structure above, it should not be removed until a temporary wall is installed (about 30 in. away from the wall). If you are removing an interior bearing wall, construct a temporary wall on both sides. A temporary supporting wall is constructed in much the same manner as a permanent wall: Studs are positioned 16 in. on centers between top and bottom plates. The main differences are that the plates are *not* nailed to the floor and ceiling, and the stud-holding nails are not toe-nailed all the way home into the plates (so they can be easily removed later).

It is important that all temporary wall studs be cut so they are a tight fit. If either ceiling or floor are uneven, use shims (undercourse shingles) between these surfaces and the plates

Installing a header

When wall studs and plates are removed, the header can be wedged up tightly under the ends of joists it will support. If required, use shims for a tight fit. If a lower header is desired, use cripple studs as shown below. The header must bear (rest) on solid wood—i.e., supporting studs, not plaster or dry wall. To make up your header, check the finished wall thickness. If the existing stud width is 3⅝ in., you'll need a ⅜-in. filler (plywood or lath) in the header

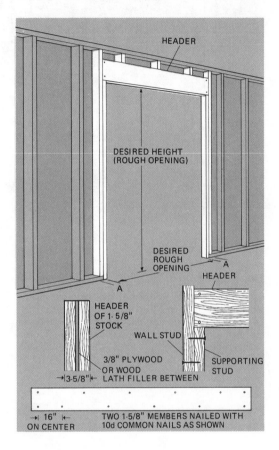

Installing new rough opening

With wall finish removed and the exact location of the desired opening determined, intermediate studs (A) may have to be installed to provide a nailer for the supporting stud or studs. With these up, the appropriate-sized header is installed, supported by a stud at each end. For openings over 6 ft., double supporting studs are required at each end of the header. For openings over 8 ft., a contractor should be employed for the job.

The chart at the bottom of the   next page is a guide for maximum loading conditions. If your room is narrower, which means less floor load, or your opening is less than that shown, your header size may be reduced. For exact sizes, consult an engineer

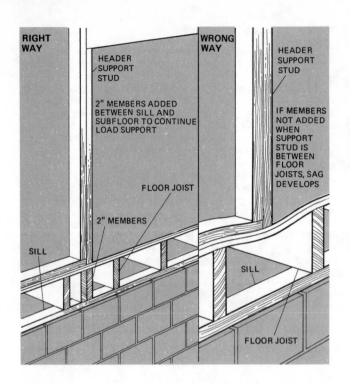

Supporting new load from below

Studs supporting the newly installed header must also bear on solid structure; they must not simply rest on flooring and subflooring or a serious sag will develop. In this event, the easiest solution is to cut short lengths of 2-in. members (1-⅝-in. actual dimension) equal in *length* to the *width* of the floor joists.

These "jacks" are then wedged—with grain running vertically—between the subflooring and the sill supporting the floor joists. If under an interior bearing wall, they're wedged between beam, or girder, and sub-flooring. Use at least two jack studs under each supporting stud and, when satisfied the fit is tight, secure jacks with 10d common nails.

In this way, the structure load is transferred from header to supporting studs through jack studs to the main support below. Once header and supports are installed and nailed, the temporary wall may be removed. The opening can now be finished on both sides to match the existing coverings

Finishing the job

Use plasterboard to re-cover the exposed studs in walls. If matching up to plaster thickness, add shims of wood to stud faces so that the drywall surface will be flush with the plaster wall. Spackle joints and nail-heads to finish. If your floor is of wood, it will be necessary to custom-fit a piece in the hole (where the old soleplate was). Fit the piece and install it with glue and nails through predrilled holes. Sand and finish

What size header do you need?

Header size is determined by span over the opening and weight it must support. In sketch of house at right, interior wall is a bearing wall. The chart lists header sizes needed for various widths in such a wall—with 12 ft. of floor on both sides. 2-in. stock now comes in 1½-in. actual dimension (old 1-⅝-in. size is still in stock at some yards)

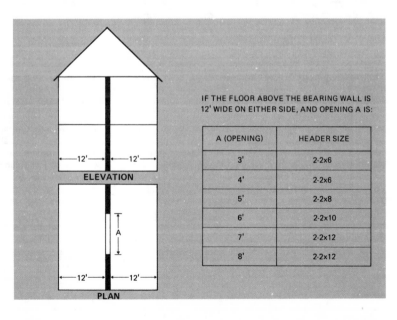

IF THE FLOOR ABOVE THE BEARING WALL IS 12' WIDE ON EITHER SIDE, AND OPENING A IS:

A (OPENING)	HEADER SIZE
3'	2-2x6
4'	2-2x6
5'	2-2x8
6'	2-2x10
7'	2-2x12
8'	2-2x12

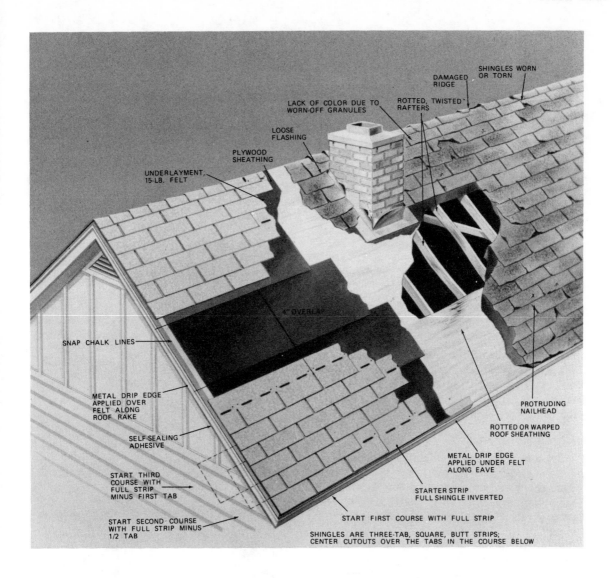

SHINGLES WORN OR TORN

DAMAGED RIDGE

LACK OF COLOR DUE TO WORN-OFF GRANULES

ROTTED, TWISTED RAFTERS

LOOSE FLASHING

PLYWOOD SHEATHING

UNDERLAYMENT, 15-LB. FELT

4" OVERLAP

SNAP CHALK LINES

METAL DRIP EDGE APPLIED OVER FELT ALONG ROOF RAKE

SELF-SEALING ADHESIVE

START THIRD COURSE WITH FULL STRIP MINUS FIRST TAB

START SECOND COURSE WITH FULL STRIP MINUS 1/2 TAB

PROTRUDING NAILHEAD

ROTTED OR WARPED ROOF SHEATHING

METAL DRIP EDGE APPLIED UNDER FELT ALONG EAVE

STARTER STRIP FULL SHINGLE INVERTED

START FIRST COURSE WITH FULL STRIP

SHINGLES ARE THREE-TAB, SQUARE, BUTT STRIPS; CENTER CUTOUTS OVER THE TABS IN THE COURSE BELOW

Roofing yourself can save half the cost

■ THE WORST ASPECT of shingling a roof is having to work *up there*. But, if you are fortunate enough to have a roof with a reasonable pitch—a ranch or Cape Cod home, for example—you might consider taking on the job and pocketing at least half of what a professional would charge.

Even if you decide to call in a pro, a good knowledge of how a roof should be applied will put you in a position to make sure that you get the job you are paying for. It's okay to put the new roof over the old, but if there are already two layers of shingles up there, the roof should be stripped and the job started from scratch. On a new roof, use 1¼-in. galvanized nails. If installing a second layer over asphalt or fiberglass shingles, up the size to 1¾-in. galvanized nails. You'll need that extra length to assure good holding power.

About asphalt shingles: The square-butt shingle measures 12x36 in., has three tabs and is nor-

SCAFFOLD HANGERS are necessary for safety. You'll need at least two pairs to work your way up the roof safely. They are attached by driving in 8d common nails after locating the bracket so that shingling can continue. To move the bracket to a new position, it is simply tapped up and the nails that held it are driven home. Use at least a 2x6 plank.

mally laid with 5 in. exposed to the weather. There are 27 strips in a bundle and three bundles make up a square (100 sq. ft.). Store the bundles of shingles flat or the strips are likely to curl as the bundles are opened for use.

Repairing old roof

Begin by checking the old roof, nailing down any loose shingles and replacing any that are damaged. If warped or rotten boards (sheathing) are present, usually under bumps or bulges, remove the shingles, replace the boards and weave in replacement shingles.

Start the reroofing by laying the valleys in first. Measure for length and cut the roll roofing. Roll the pieces up and place a roll at each valley. (Your local code might require the use of metal flashing instead of roll roofing.) Width of flashing to use in a valley is determined by roof pitch. The usual is 12 inches wide for slopes of 7 inches in 12 and over; 18 inches wide for 4 inches in 12 to 7 inches in 12 slopes and 24 inches for slopes less than 4 inches in 12.

After applying 15-lb. felt with staples, the starter course can go down. It can be either wood, asphalt or fiberglass shingles (applied upside down) as in the drawing. In any event, the starter course should be applied so it projects at least ½ in. over the eaves. This will prevent water from running back up under the shingles. A ½-in. shingle projection should also be used at the rake (gable) ends.

The shingles are applied on up to the ridge and once all shingles are in place, they can be trimmed at the valleys. Measure at least 2 in.

either side of the valley center at the top and 3 or 4 in. both sides at the bottom (eaves). Drive a nail at each of these four spots, attach a chalkline and snap to determine where shingles should be cut.

Use a piece of ⅜-in. plywood *under* the shingles along the valley. Place the carpenter's square along the chalkline on top of the shingles and cut with your utility knife. Remove cutaway pieces, finish nailing the trimmed shingles and apply roof cement to the edges.

Capping at the ridge can be done with a 12-in.-wide strip of roll roofing. But it is more common to use full shingles cut into thirds. These are

ROOFING TOOLS materials (top) are shingles, roof cement and roll roofing. The correct way to walk on a pitched roof (shown directly above) is with weight concentrated on the edge of feet toward the down side. Rubber-soled shoes are essential.

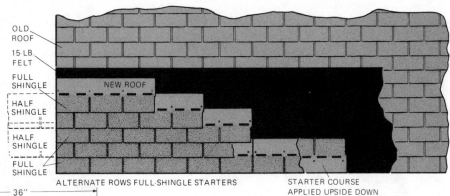

OLD ROOF
15-LB. FELT
FULL SHINGLE
NEW ROOF
HALF SHINGLE
HALF SHINGLE
FULL SHINGLE
ALTERNATE ROWS FULL-SHINGLE STARTERS
STARTER COURSE APPLIED UPSIDE DOWN

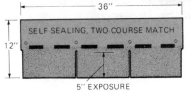

36"
12"
SELF SEALING, TWO-COURSE MATCH
5" EXPOSURE

TAB SHINGLES are always applied so that the full tab is centered over a slot below. If length of the roof requires a narrow piece to finish the first course, start the second row with a piece of the same width. Then continue alternating narrow pieces in each succeeding row all the way to the ridge of the roof.

VALLEY TREATMENT

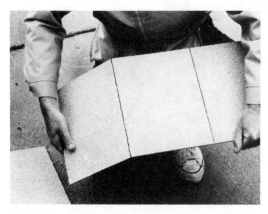

TO CUT an asphalt shingle, score a line with your utility knife, then bend and snap off the piece.

A TYPICAL open valley goes quickly if you use a chalkline to determine the exact angle cutoffs on shingles.

ROLL ROOFING, FACE UP
CHALK LINES
ASPHALT CEMENT
15 LB. FELT

OPEN VALLEY is flashed with 38-in.-wide roll roofing before you move up the roof with the shingle courses. (Note: Some building codes require the use of metal flashing; see text). Width of the valley between courses should increase from top to the bottom. Minimum open width at the top is 4 in. between courses.

VALLEY SHINGLES are trimmed at one time using a straight-edge on the chalkline and a utility knife.

then applied as shown in the photos. Notice that the final ridge shingle receives four nails. Make certain you seal the exposed nailheads with roof cement.

Notice that the shingles shown have adhesive patches above the tabs. These are a sealer-type shingle that will withstand greater wind and rain forces than non-sealer-type shingles. This built-in advantage makes them well worth the few extra dollars of cost.

Words of caution. For maximum traction, use rubber-soled shoes or sneakers when roofing. And don't walk on the edges of the shingles because you are apt to crack them. Instead, place your feet squarely on shingle centers.

WATERPROOFING A STACK

PLASTIC ROOF cement is used to seal the joint around stack in roof. Cement is applied with a putty knife (a wood shingle will also work fine) after shingles are trimmed for a neat job. If desired, paint the cement to match.

RIDGE TREATMENT

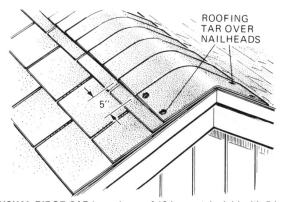

ROOFING TAR OVER NAILHEADS

5″

USUAL RIDGE CAP is made up of 12-in.-sq. tabs laid with 5-in. exposure to the weather. These can be cut on the ground and carried up by the armful. Each tab is applied with two nails— except for the last shingle. Here, four nails are used and the exposed heads are then waterproofed with dabs of cement.

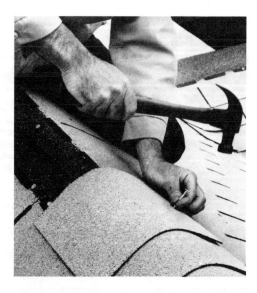

Damaged roof repair

■ HIGH WINDS and heavy rains are never welcomed by homeowners. When such storms strike, most of us consider ourselves lucky if damage to the house and property is minor. Unfortunately, very often the damage is up on the roof. Shingles that have been exposed to weather for 10 years or more are particularly susceptible to being blown off. (However, the self-seal, tab-type shingles, which have been around a while, have reduced the incidence of this type of damage considerably.) Of far great-

er concern is what to do when your roof—not just the shingles—has been damaged by a toppled tree or fallen limb.

If you are afraid of height and working from a ladder, don't fight the feeling: Call in a pro. But if you do the repair work yourself, be advised it is a must to thoroughly cut out all the damaged area and replace with sound material. New sheathing must be of the same thickness as the existing, and all joints must be properly covered with 15-lb. felt. Weaving-in of shingles is a must or the patched-in area will leak.

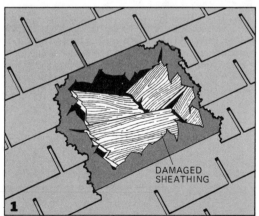

SEVERE ROOF DAMAGE, such as shattered sheathing shown here, can be caused by falling limbs. Sheathing problems can also result from leakage, which rots sheathing. Rot damage is often not apparent. If you spot a bulge under the shingles, chances are the sheathing needs replacing. Inspect the area from inside where possible.

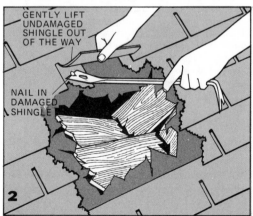

DAMAGED SHINGLES and tarpaper (felt) must be entirely—and cleanly—removed. Completely remove any partially damaged shingle so you can weave in a replacement shingle. Start with top course and work down. Use a ripping bar or large screwdriver to pry up nails from damaged shingle, or tear out shingle and drive nails home.

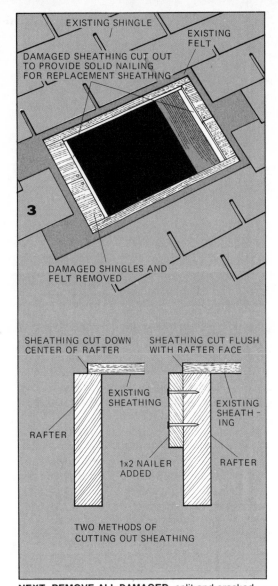

EXISTING SHINGLE

EXISTING FELT

DAMAGED SHEATHING CUT OUT TO PROVIDE SOLID NAILING FOR REPLACEMENT SHEATHING

3

DAMAGED SHINGLES AND FELT REMOVED

SHEATHING CUT DOWN CENTER OF RAFTER

SHEATHING CUT FLUSH WITH RAFTER FACE

EXISTING SHEATHING

EXISTING SHEATH-ING

RAFTER

1x2 NAILER ADDED

RAFTER

TWO METHODS OF CUTTING OUT SHEATHING

NEXT, REMOVE ALL DAMAGED, split and cracked sheathing to obtain a squared, easy-to-fit opening. You need solid nailing to attach new sheathing; use either method above to cut out old. Either cut down center of a rafter or cut alongside and add a 1x2 nailer for the new sheathing to be fastened to. The latter method is easier.

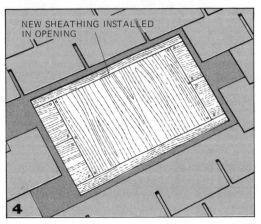

NEW SHEATHING INSTALLED IN OPENING

4

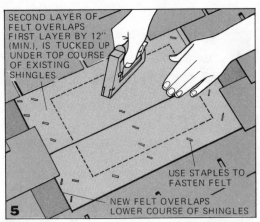

SECOND LAYER OF FELT OVERLAPS FIRST LAYER BY 12" (MIN.), IS TUCKED UP UNDER TOP COURSE OF EXISTING SHINGLES

USE STAPLES TO FASTEN FELT

NEW FELT OVERLAPS LOWER COURSE OF SHINGLES

5

APPLY 15-pound felt so it overlaps existing shingles on downside and is tucked under row at top. Completely cover joints discussed in Step 4 and slip felt beneath shingles to right and left. Apply felt with 12-in. overlap, making sure it's flat or shingles will bulge. Use ample number of ¼-in. staples to secure felt.

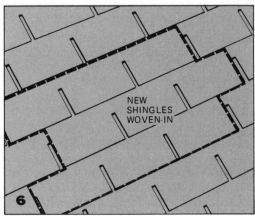

NEW SHINGLES WOVEN-IN

6

WEAVE NEW SHINGLES into existing ones so alternate rows overlap. *Never have an unbroken vertical line (shingle joint).* Here, for clarity, new shingles are shown slightly lighter than the existing. On repair jobs, take a piece of old shingle when you buy the new. Try to match so your repair job will be virtually invisible.

USE EITHER 1x6 tongue-and-groove roofers or plywood as shown, but it must be same thickness as existing sheathing. Plywood goes faster because it requires cutting just one piece (for a small hole). Next, cut 8-in.-wide felt strips and cover joints. Do bottom horizontal first, then the verticals and top horizontal; use overlaps.

TRY TO drive nails flush with shingle's surface but not so hard that the nailheads will crush the wood.

Reroof with wood shakes and shingles

■ MANY HOMEOWNERS still prefer the rustic, colonial beauty of a wood-shingle roof in preference to asphalt, and if your home has such a roof which needs reshingling with either red-cedar shakes or shingles, a little know-how is all it takes for you to do the job yourself with professional results. You can end up saving yourself a lot of money and have a handsome finished product.

Called the aristocrat of roofing materials, handsplit cedar shakes make a luxurious roof of

MAXIMUM EXPOSURE FOR WOOD SHAKES

TYPE	THICKNESS	LENGTH	DOUBLE COVERAGE	TRIPLE COVERAGE
Handsplit and resawn shakes	½ to ¾" ½ to ¾" ¾ to 1¼"	18" 24" 32"	8½" 10" 13"	5½" 7½" 10"
Tapersplit shakes	½ to ⅝"	24"	10"	7½"
Straightsplit shakes	⅜" ⅜"	18" 24"		5½" 7½"

unsurpassed durability that will actually outlast the house itself. Shakes may be applied directly over the old roof if it's not slate, tile or "asbestos." Where the old roof is to remain, 6-in. strips of the old roofing are removed along the eaves and gables, and replaced with 1x6 boards before the shakes are laid. These boards provide a strong base at the perimeter, concealing the old roof from view.

Over-roofing, of course, has a number of advantages. It gives extra insulation. You don't have to worry about sudden rains while applying the shingles, and there's a lot less litter to pick up from the lawn and shrubs. But where you might be fixing up an old dilapidated house with a beyond-saving shingle roof, you have no recourse but to strip the roof and start from scratch. You have a choice of three kinds of shakes.

• *Handsplit and resawn shakes* have split faces and sawn backs. After cedar logs are cut into the desired length, blanks of proper thickness are split, and these then are run diagonally through a band-saw to produce two tapered shakes from each blank.

• *Tapersplit shakes* are produced entirely by hand, using a sharp-bladed knife called a froe and a wooden mallet. A natural shinglelike taper, from butt to tip, is achieved by reversing the block, end for end, with each split.

• *Straightsplit or barn shakes* are made in the same manner as taper-split shakes, except that the splitting is done from one end of the block only. This produces shakes which are the same thickness throughout.

Applying shakes

Shakes can be applied over open or solid sheathing, although in areas where wind-driven snow is encountered, solid sheathing is recommended. For good drainage, the pitch (slope) of your roof should not be less than one-sixth, or 4-in-12 (4 in. vertical rise for each 12-in. horizontal run). The correct weather exposure is important too, and the chart gives the maximum exposure for standard 18, 24 and 32-in. shakes, in double and triple coverages. Note that the ⅜ x 24-in. shakes should be applied at 7½-in. exposure when the roof pitch is less than 8-in-12.

To begin, a 36-in.-wide strip of 30-lb. roofing felt is laid over the sheathing boards at the eave line. The starter course of shakes is doubled, the bottom course being 15 or 18-in. shakes expressly made for the purpose. Wood shakes should extend 1 to 1½ in. out over the eave and rake to form a drip. After each course is completed, an 18-in.-wide strip of felt is placed over the top portion of the shakes. Here the bottom edge of the felt is kept above the shake butts a

ROOF APPLICATION

18", 30-LB. FELT

DOUBLE STARTER COURSE

VALLEYS

METAL VALLEY SHEETS, 20" MINIMUM

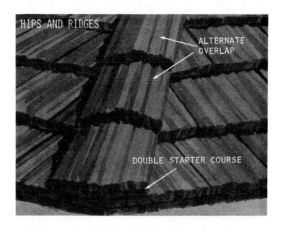

HIPS AND RIDGES

ALTERNATE OVERLAP

DOUBLE STARTER COURSE

distance equal to twice the weather exposure. For example, if 24-in. shakes are being laid at a 10-in. exposure, the felt should be positioned 20 in. above the shake butts. The strip will then cover the top 4 in. of the shakes and extend 14 in. onto the sheathing. The individual shakes should be spaced ¼ to ⅜ in. to allow for possible expansion, and the joint offset at least 1½ in. in adjacent courses.

Fasten each shake with just two nails and use only rust-resistant nails (hot-dipped zinc or aluminum) driven 1 in. from each edge and 1 or 2 in. above the butt line of the course to follow. A 2-in. (6-penny) nail normally is adequate, but longer nails should be used when shake thickness dictates. Drive the nails until the heads meet the shake surface but *no further*; nails have less holding power when the heads are driven into the shake.

For the final course at the ridge line, uniform shakes are selected. A strip of roofing felt, at least 8 in. wide, is applied over the crown of all hips and ridges and shakes approximately 6-in. wide are sorted out to cover them. Two straightedges are tacked to the roof, 5 in. each side of the center line of the hip.

CHIMNEY FLASHING

MAXIMUM EXPOSURE FOR WOOD SHINGLES

ROOF SLOPE	SHINGLE LENGTHS		
	16″	18″	24″
5 in 12 or steeper	5″	5½″	7½″
4 in 12	4½″	5″	6¾″
3 in 12	3¾″	4¼″	5¾″

NAIL SIZES RECOMMENDED

SIZE	LENGTH	GAUGE	HEAD	SHINGLES
3d*	1-¼″	14-½	⁷/₃₂″	16 & 18″
4d*	1-½″	14	⁷/₃₂″	24″
5d**	1-¾″	14	⁷/₃₂″	
6d**	2″	13	⁷/₃₂″	

*3d and 4d nails used for new construction
**5d and 6d nails used for reroofing

The bottom course of hip shakes is doubled and the butts are trimmed to align with the starting courses at the eaves. The first hip shake is nailed in place with one edge resting against the guide strip. Then the portion projecting over the center of the hip is cut back on a bevel. The shake on the opposite side is then applied and its projecting edge is cut back to fit. Shakes in following courses are applied alternately in reverse order. Weather exposure of the hip shakes should be the same as that for the roof shakes.

All valleys should be underlaid with 30-lb. roofing felt applied over the sheathing. The metal valley sheets should be at least 20 in. wide. Edges of the shakes are cut to run parallel up the valleys, approximately 5 in. apart. Base and chimney flashing units are laid with each shake course and counterflashed.

An adjustable exposure gauge on the edge of a shingler's hatchet speeds application in making it easy to measure correct exposure and run the courses straight.

Applying red-cedar shingles

Red-cedar shingles are applied in much the same manner as shakes. Where they are to be applied over an old roof of wood or asphalt shingles, roof preparation is the same along the eaves and gables. In addition, a strip of lumber is laid in each valley to separate the old metal valley from the new, and the old ridge shingles are replaced with strips of beveled cedar siding, thin edge downward.

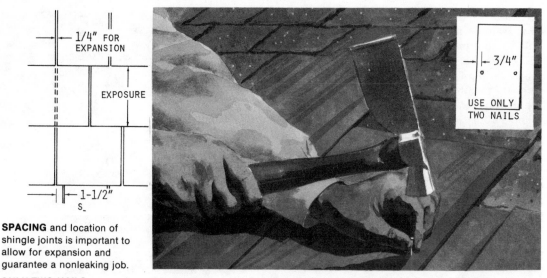

1/4" FOR EXPANSION

EXPOSURE

1-1/2"
S

3/4"

USE ONLY TWO NAILS

SPACING and location of shingle joints is important to allow for expansion and guarantee a nonleaking job.

ONLY TWO NAILS are used per shingle and are placed so they are ¾ in. above butts of following course.

Normally, cedar shingles are applied in straight single courses, using a straightedge to keep the rows straight and true. On roof slopes of 5-in-12 and steeper, standard exposures are: 5 in. for 16-in. shingles, 5½ in. for 18-in. shingles and 7½ in. for 24 in. shingles. If the roof pitch is less than 3-in-12, cedar shingles are not recommended.

Like shakes, cedar shingles are doubled along the eaves, and the butts of the first course are laid so they hang over the edge 1½ in. to insure proper rain spillage in the gutters.

Space the shingles ¼ in. apart and never have two joints in line if separated by only one course of shingles. Leave a side-lap of 1½ in. between joints in successive courses. Use only two nails

10' 10'

TO ESTIMATE the number of shingles needed for your roof, four bundles, which are called a ''square,'' will normally cover 100 square feet of roof area.

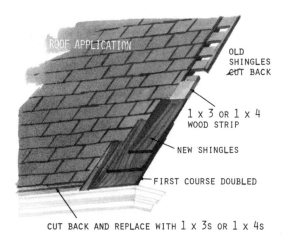

ROOF APPLICATION

OLD SHINGLES CUT BACK

1 x 3 OR 1 x 4 WOOD STRIP

NEW SHINGLES

FIRST COURSE DOUBLED

CUT BACK AND REPLACE WITH 1 x 3s OR 1 x 4s

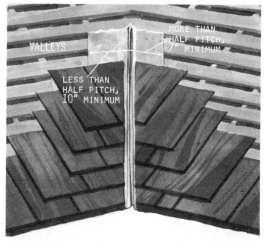

VALLEYS

MORE THAN HALF PITCH, 7" MINIMUM

LESS THAN HALF PITCH, 10" MINIMUM

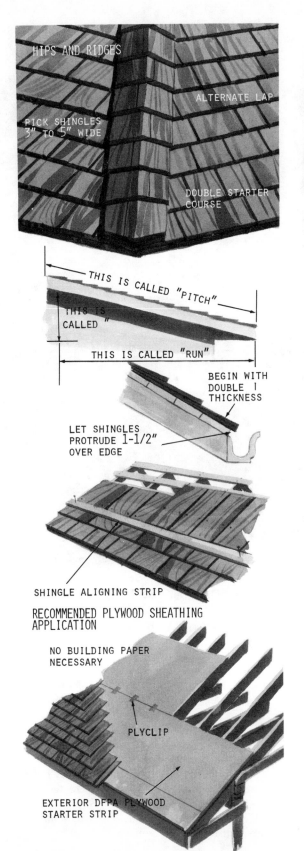

HIPS AND RIDGES

ALTERNATE LAP

PICK SHINGLES 3" TO 5" WIDE

DOUBLE STARTER COURSE

CHIMNEY FLASHING

THIS IS CALLED "PITCH"

THIS IS CALLED " "

THIS IS CALLED "RUN"

BEGIN WITH DOUBLE THICKNESS

LET SHINGLES PROTRUDE 1-1/2" OVER EDGE

SHINGLE ALIGNING STRIP

RECOMMENDED PLYWOOD SHEATHING APPLICATION

NO BUILDING PAPER NECESSARY

PLYCLIP

EXTERIOR DFPA PLYWOOD STARTER STRIP

per shingle, ¾ in. in from each edge, and locate them so the next course will cover the nails by at least ¾ in. The chart specifies the right size of nail to use. As with shakes, the use of rust-resistant nails is most important. Drive the nails flush, but not so hard the nailheads crush the wood.

Hips and ridges are capped with factory-assembled units lapped to provide the same exposure as in the roof proper.

Estimating squares

A "square" of shingles consists of four bundles, so called because they normally will cover 100 square feet of roof area.

To estimate the number of squares you'll have to order for your roof, first determine the square-foot ground area of your house (include eave and cornice overhang). Increase this total square-foot area by 8½ percent if the roof pitch is 5 in 12, 12 percent if it's 6 in 12 or 20 percent if 8 in 12. Then divide total by 100.

Where pitch is less than 5 in 12, allow for a third more shingles to compensate for the reduced exposure. And, add a square for each 100 lineal feet of hips and valleys. As for nails, figure 2½ lbs. per 100 sq. ft. of roof area.

Before you get on any roof, slip on a pair of sneakers. They'll not only give you good footing, but they'll keep you from marking up your new roof.

Walls that serve a purpose

■ AS YOUR FAMILY GROWS, so does the accumulation of personal possessions. It becomes increasingly clear that the more square feet of living space in your home you can utilize efficiently, the greater your family comfort will be. A logical, and frequently the most economical, place to turn to for desperately needed storage space is a wall. The three wall ideas shown here, in addition to satisfying particular family storage needs, have something else in common: Each is well-designed and adds to the looks and the value of the home.

The long see-through wall shown above is framed to give a deck (or counter) at a height of approximately 36 in. The deck and post enclosures are of nominal 1-in. clear pine. The cabinet on the living room side was paneled; on the opposite side narrow pine shelves were installed to hold a collection of knickknacks.

Above the deck, large dowels (closet poles) were installed to give the illusion of greater room height and size. Thus, several advantages were gained by converting a flat, run-of-the-mill wall into a customized "room divider."

The unit shown at the bottom of this page was designed by a pro. The homeowners required a built-in that could be used for stereo equipment and a convenient closet for their children to store boots, mittens and so forth. Additionally, they wanted it placed near the front entrance to create an entry way.

The cabinet is 27 in. wide, 39 in. high and 42 in. long. In turn, it is topped by a double-deck set of 18 hand-turned balusters (nine per row). The folding doors on the living-room side are trimmed with factory-made moldings for a decorator touch and fitted with friction catches for easy access. The interior shelves are removable; thus, should storage needs ever change, there is a built-in flexibility to meet them.

The children's side of the cabinet, by the front door, is fitted with sliding doors for quick use. Inside, there is an accordion-type wood hanger with peg hooks for small-fry clothes plus the storage for boots and the like. To match the existing decor in the room, the entire cabinet-divider unit was painted a Wedgwood blue shade.

The third unit shown was designed expressly to handle the storage needs in a playroom next to a kitchen. It's a built-in along a wall, 15 feet long, that has been divided into five equal sections. Each of the five youngsters in the family, from toddler to teen-ager, has his own personal storage area.

Horizontal members are spaced so as to create 13 sections (plus a pass-through to the kitchen for snack serving.). Six of the sections are fitted with doors to protect the older children's more valuable games and possessions from the little ones' inquisitive hands. The remaining lower sections are fitted with 18-in. adjustable shelves.

ENTRY WALL, viewed below from both sides, provides storage area for stereo components, closet for children's wardrobe and attractive foyer at the front door.

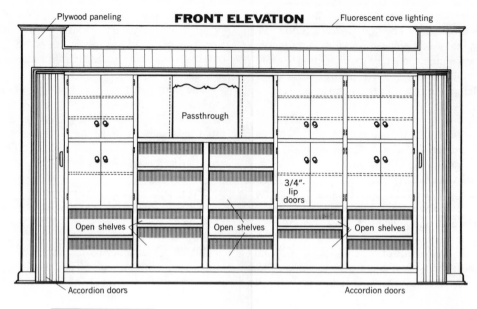

FRONT ELEVATION

Plywood paneling

Fluorescent cove lighting

Passthrough

3/4"-lip doors

Open shelves   Open shelves   Open shelves

Accordion doors   Accordion doors

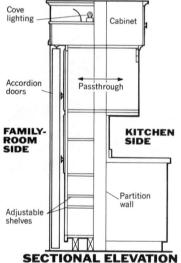

Cove lighting

Cabinet

Accordion doors

Passthrough

FAMILY-ROOM SIDE   **KITCHEN SIDE**

Partition wall

Adjustable shelves

SECTIONAL ELEVATION

FULL-DEPTH wall gives ample storage required by a large family. Accordion doors hide it all when desired.

The unit shown was constructed entirely of ¾-in. plywood (except for cleats, nailers and the like). To withstand abuse, the unit was finished, inside and out, with a primer and semigloss paint.

To hide the unavoidable clutter of toys that always seems to be present on the toddler's open shelves, accordion doors were installed in front. Then, when the room is used for adult parties, the paraphernalia behind can be quickly removed from view.

If the wall is to be used primarily by adults or teen-agers, the face of the unit could be built of cabinet-grade plywood and stained for a natural finish. Another method would be to treat the facing with either ½-in. plywood or particleboard, and then glue and nail prefinished paneling over.

Freestanding wall lets you divide and conquer

■ A PERFECT "space-doubler" for youngsters sharing the same bedroom, this freestanding wall clearly draws the line between activity and sleeping areas. Gone will be the nightly squabbles over

the right time for lights out—and your role as arbiter, happily, will be vastly diminished.

Don't get discouraged about building this project because you have never built a wall before. You needn't be a master carpenter or own any special tools to test your do-it-yourself skills on this project. The wall consists of a 2x4 framework covered on one side with plasterboard and wallpaper, and on the other side with a durable ¼-in. prefinished plywood paneling.

As in conventional house building, the easiest way to build a wall is to assemble it flat on the floor. To prevent the wall from racking (going out of square), the plywood paneling should be applied to one side while the wall is still in the horizontal position. The wall can then be tilted upright and held with diagonal braces while the plasterboard and wallpaper are applied to the second side.

There are two slight differences between this wall and the walls of your house. First, it is *not* fastened to the floor. This means that you will not be tied down to one furniture-layout scheme. Instead, a piece of ¾-in. plywood, which is attached inconspicuously to the bed frame, is in turn screw-fastened to the wall (see the inset drawing on the next page).

The second important thing to keep in mind is that the wall should stop short of ceiling height by about one foot in most homes. If it did not, the resulting look would be wall rather than divider. Before starting construction, make certain you measure bedroom floor-to-ceiling height and scale your divider to it (as well as scaling the divider width to bed width).

A BRIGHT, SOPHISTICATED bedroom becomes more functional when space is divided into logical-use areas. Here, wall facing study-play area carries a durable, prefinished plywood paneling; its other side is plasterboard, wallpapered to match the bedspread and the draperies.

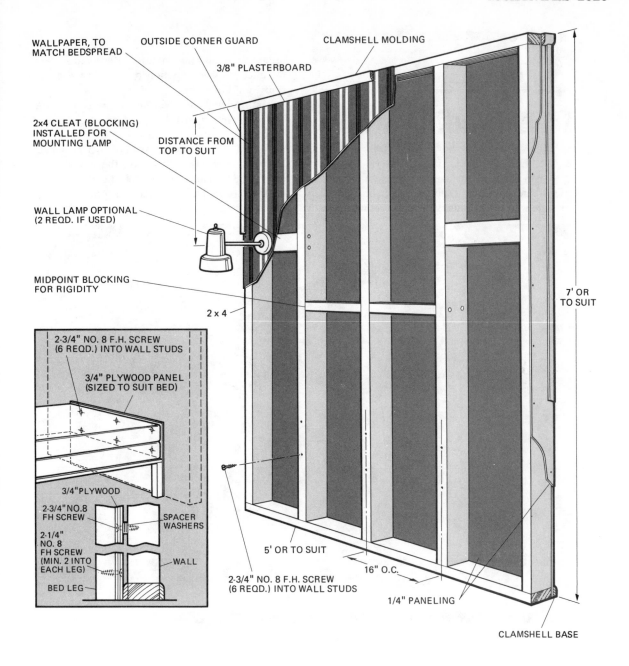

WALLPAPER, TO MATCH BEDSPREAD

OUTSIDE CORNER GUARD

CLAMSHELL MOLDING

3/8" PLASTERBOARD

2x4 CLEAT (BLOCKING) INSTALLED FOR MOUNTING LAMP

DISTANCE FROM TOP TO SUIT

WALL LAMP OPTIONAL (2 REQD. IF USED)

MIDPOINT BLOCKING FOR RIGIDITY

2 x 4

7' OR TO SUIT

2-3/4" NO. 8 F.H. SCREW (6 REQD.) INTO WALL STUDS

3/4" PLYWOOD PANEL (SIZED TO SUIT BED)

3/4" PLYWOOD

2-3/4" NO.8 FH SCREW

SPACER WASHERS

2-1/4" NO. 8 FH SCREW (MIN. 2 INTO EACH LEG)

WALL

BED LEG

2-3/4" NO. 8 F.H. SCREW (6 REQD.) INTO WALL STUDS

5' OR TO SUIT

16" O.C.

1/4" PANELING

CLAMSHELL BASE

The wall facing the active area is most likely to receive some punishment from lively youngsters. Thus, it is clad with the same plywood paneling used on the bedroom walls. Paneling here also gives a feeling of continuity—that the wall is an integral part of the room. Lacking such coordination, it might look like an afterthought.

The second side is covered with ⅜-in. plaster-board. Joints and dimpled nailheads are hidden with two applications of joint compound and the wall is finished with wallpaper to match bedspread and draperies. Conventional molding at top, base and corners supplies the finishing touches. If desired, battery-powered pin-up lamps can be installed on the divider over the bed.

Light a freestanding wall

■ **INSTEAD OF THE USUAL** fluorescent fixture light for the light over a freestanding wall, use 10 incandescent ceiling receptacles. These provide warmer lighting. Conventional wiring is used to build the fixture. Receptacles are mounted on 4-in. junction boxes and BX cable runs from box to box.

Fixture length is determined by need. In the 7-footer shown, 10 *low-wattage* bulbs were used, spaced equidistant and staggered on opposite sides. The frame consists of two 2x6s held together by ¾x1-in. strips on the bottom and ends. The translucent sheet plastic simply rests on the strips. The end piece, of course, is secured with cleats.

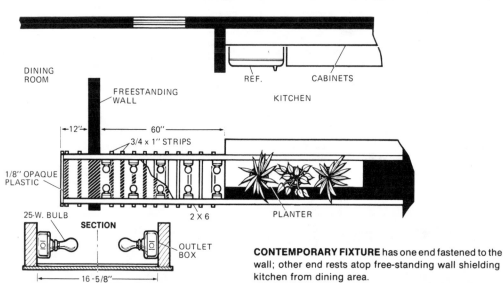

DINING ROOM

FREESTANDING WALL

REF.   CABINETS

KITCHEN

←12″→   ←——60″——→

¾ x 1″ STRIPS

1/8″ OPAQUE PLASTIC

2 X 6

PLANTER

25-W. BULB

SECTION

OUTLET BOX

←— 16 -5/8″ —→

CONTEMPORARY FIXTURE has one end fastened to the wall; other end rests atop free-standing wall shielding kitchen from dining area.

Router techniques

■ IF YOU HAVEN'T already tried one because you felt—as many workshoppers do—that a router is beyond your skills, be advised it's one of the greatest power tools you can get your hands on.

Undeservedly, the router has the reputation of being difficult to handle. The plain fact is that it's one of the easiest-to-use and most satisfying power tools you will ever handle.

Mechanically, the router is simple; it consists of two pieces, a motor with a chuck mounted on one end and a base that holds the tool in a vertical position for routing. A bit or cutter is mounted in the chuck and protrudes down to do the cutting. The maximum depth of cut is determined by length of the cutter being used. The high speed of the router—anywhere from 20,000 to 28,000 rpm—teamed with a clean, sharp cutter will generally produce a cut so smooth that further sanding is unnecessary.

In essence, a router does much the same work as a stationary shaper *with two differences;* the tool is carried to the job, instead of the other way around, and a router can be used for on-the-job tasks such as hinge-mortising and trimming plastic laminates. (The router is the only way to go if you do a lot of plastic laminating.) If equipped with the proper bit(s), a router can be used on nonferrous metals.

Router safety

General power-tool safety rules apply to the router. For example, make certain that the tool is properly grounded if it's not of the double-insulated variety; keep the tool, motor and cutters clean (always being sure that the motor's air vents are not clogged by sawdust), and, because of the flying chips that the tool creates, always wear safety goggles.

Good safety habits you should acquire include: 1) always disconnect the electric cord when installing or removing a cutter; 2) make certain that the piece to be worked is securely clamped; 3) double check to assure that *all* adjustments are tightened before turning on the motor—you should *never make any adjustments while the router is running;* 4) hold the router firmly at all times; 5) though it may seem obvious, as you finish a job and turn off power, place the router on its side on your workbench and hold it until the cutter stops spinning.

Router bits and accessories

The first rule regarding bits and accessories—and it's a must—is to use only those cutters and accessories specifically designed for use in high-speed routers. Much of the router's versatility comes from the variety of bits and cutters now available. (One major manufacturer claims there are more than 170 cutters on the market.) Many bits sold today are originally designed to suit specific commercial needs. Ultimately, these special-purpose bits found their way into home workshops.

In simplest terms, there are three types of bits:

• *Pilot type* (such as the edge-rabbet cutter) is a one-piece bit that has a cutter portion and a pilot at bottom which rides against the work edge while the cutter does its chore. Bits for decorative edge-trimming are of this design.

• *Cutters used for grooving* (mortise-type). These do not have a pilot, and the cutting edge extends full length of the cutter. To use these bits (except when freehand cutting), it is necessary to use a guide: either an improvised clamped-on piece of wood or the factory-made version which is attached to the router.

• *Panel bits,* which have a drill-type tip. These are used when it is desirable to plunge through the workpiece and then begin routing the design.

As mentioned above, variations on the basic cutters are almost endless. And now most mak-

SIMPLEST OF ALL power tools, the router consists of two basic pieces—the motor with a chuck on one end of its shaft and a base to hold it.

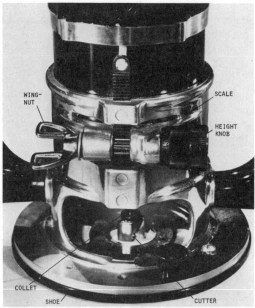

MOST ROUTERS have a quick-read depth indicator plus a method of adjustment for precision settings.

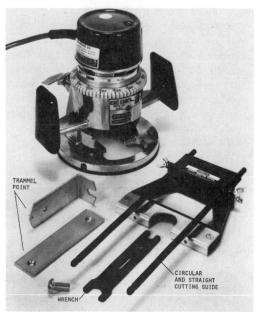

TWO NECESSARY accessories are a trammel point (left) for circle cutting and a straight cutting guide.

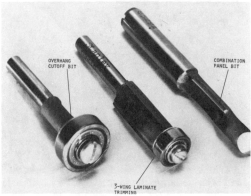

THESE THREE BITS aren't cheap but well worth the investment for a steady router user.

ROUTER-BIT case keeps bits where you can find them and protects the cutting edges.

DOOR-AND-JAMB butt template is a timesaver for a professional who wants to hang many doors in a hurry.

ers are offering almost all types in a carbide version. Like saw blades, these cost more initially, but for the frequent user, they are worth extra cash outlay. If your shop production is limited however, you are probably better off buying noncarbide bits and having them sharpened occasionally.

A router without accessories could be compared to a bench saw equipped with a combination blade only. For example, you need attachments to guide the machine for straight and circular work (when using nonpilot-type bits). The straight guide is invaluable when making grooves and dadoes. And using a trammel point, you'll find you can quickly cut the neatest, most accurate circles in the least time.

You can—and in many cases you must—make your own accessories. For example, a long board fitted to the router shoe will let you safely straddle the cut portion when you are cutting an extra-wide groove. But, generally, the manufactured accessories are in such an economical price range that it makes good sense to buy them.

Installing the cutters

After selecting the bit you are going to use, loosen the collet locknut. Insert the bit all the way into the collet, finger-tighten the locknut, then back out the bit about ⅛ in. (This procedure is to prevent the collet from shattering.) Place the motor on the workbench and slip one wrench over the chuck and hold its end against the benchtop. Holding the chuck with this wrench, tighten collet with the second wrench. (Note: Some routers are designed so the collet can be tightened with one wrench. On these, the arbor is locked by means provided on the router motor.) To remove a router bit, simply reverse the procedure.

Loosen the locking nut on the base and install the motor. Adjust the motor so the cutter is at desired depth and tighten the base locking nut. All quality routers have a ring or other means for

INSTALLING THE CUTTER

AFTER DISCONNECTING the power, insert the bit fully into the router chuck and then back it out ⅛ in.

TOOL is placed on bench and one wrench is slipped onto the chuck while second wrench tightens the locknut.

CORRECT WAY TO FEED A ROUTER INTO WORKPIECE

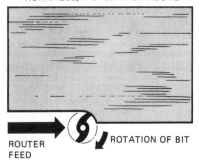

WORKPIECE, VIEWED FROM ABOVE

ROUTER FEED · ROTATION OF BIT

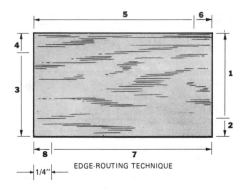

EDGE-ROUTING TECHNIQUE

SINCE MOTOR rotates clockwise, move the router from left to right. The sequence at right saves splintered corners.

CUTTING GROOVES AND DADOES

TO CUT groove, it is necessary to guide the router. Here, a commercially made guide is being used.

IF CUT must be farther away from the guide, a clamped wood strip—which handles clear—works well.

making fine, precise depth adjustments. Consult the maker's manual to determine how to make fine adjustments on your router.

Direction of feed and thrust

Viewed from above, the router cutter spins in a clockwise direction. Thus, the router should be

EDGE-RABBET cutter (foreground) has a pilot that rides against workpiece edge while rabbet is formed.

moved from left to right; this allows you to cut against bit rotation. Feed rate and depth of cut to use will depend a great deal on the material being worked. If possible, make test passes on scraps of the same stock. Keep feed pressure constant, and do not force the router because you will slow down the motor excessively. This will give a poor cut—rough and, in all likelihood, cutter-burn spots. More important, it's unfair to the tool and will shorten its life.

On particularly hard woods or problem materials, your best bet is to make the cut (or cuts) in several passes, lowering the cutter for each successive pass.

When edge-routing with a pilot bit, follow the sequence as shown in the drawing. That is, start the first side ¼ in. in from the corner and feed through to the right-hand corner. Then return to the starting point and plough off the ¼ in. at the left-hand corner. Repeat these steps around sides two, three and four. The first four passes are across the end grain and the next four with the grain. By using this sequence you'll have splinter-free corners.

Grooves and dadoes

Two of the most basic cuts in woodworking can be easily, quickly and neatly made with a properly handled router and accessories. The important points to remember are that the router cannot be allowed to drift or walk away from the

FOR WIDE grooves, tack two boards to limit the router's travel and clamp work to bench for safety.

TO CUT groove in narrow piece, clamp work between two scrap pieces of wood that provide shoe support.

guide. And the shoe must always have ample, solid surface to ride on (so it won't rock on the workpiece). As can be seen in the photos, these are easy-to-make cuts. In all probability, these will be the first that you will attempt with your new router.

After you have familiarized yourself with your router by making some test grooves and dadoes, you may want to try some different cuts.

The simplest and most common cutting done with a router (right behind the two cuts mentioned above) is decorative edging. It's about the quickest, surest way to add a professional touch to any project.

Decorative edging

A shaped edge, whether Roman ogee, beaded or simply rounded-over (quarter round), improves the looks of just about any cabinet door, tabletop or drawer front. Actually, doing these edges goes so effortlessly that it is easy to give in to the temptation to put an edge on just about everything in sight. To avoid the mistake of *over-routing,* decide *which* edges will receive *what* treatment—and stick to the plan.

Bit versatility can be increased by simply raising or lowering the cutter. You can put decorative edges on circular workpieces, too. To do it, use the circle-cutting guide and counterclockwise feed.

When in doubt, feed the router extra slowly.

As you gain experience, you'll find that many woods have a tendency to splinter off large pieces ahead of the cutter. A slow feed rate and sharp cutter usually prevent this happening, but if it still happens, you should make the decorative edge with several passes. Lower the bit for each succeeding pass until the desired shape (depth) is achieved.

A lipped door is easily made using the ding-over and rabbet-cutter bits. But sequence is important: Make the rounded edge first, then the rabbet. Since the rabbet cutter's pilot will not have a surface to bear against, affix a guide for the router sub-base (shoe) when cutting the rabbets.

Circular work

Circles cut with a router will be absolutely accurate. The photos show a perfect circle being cut from plywood using a trammel point and panel-type bit; the other is a decorative plaque created by routing concentric circles with trammel point and core-box bits of various radii set at a different depth for each circle. Variations on this type of design are almost unlimited; each bit at a different cutting depth will provide a visual difference.

Plastic laminates

Because of looks and durability, plastic laminates are now commonly used by do-ityourselfers. But plastic-laminate fabrication requires precise workmanship. Since plastic laminates are not cheap, it makes good sense to practice on scrap before you put your router to an actual project.

Since conventional steel bits won't hold cutting edges if used on plastics, *always* use a carbide bit. Cutting edges on carbide-tipped bits hold up indefinitely and, more important, give neat, chipfree cuts. Of two types—one-piece solid and self-contained ball-bearing—you'll need two (of either design): a straight cutter for overhang trimming and a bevel bit (varying from 15° to 22°) to finish-dress the joint.

If you prefer the one-piece solid, smear petroleum jelly on the laminated self-edge to avoid any chance of the cutter creating a scorch mark. But if you have the ball-bearing type, acquire the habit of frequently disassembling parts and cleaning them with lacquer thinner. Then oil and reassemble. If you don't, the bearing eventually clogs with contact cement and spins at the same speed as the cutter—and then it will leave a burned line along the self-edge. The bearing *must* be free-spinning so it will rotate at the speed of router movement—*not the cutting flutes.*

Make sure that edges of the material to which the laminate will be cemented are square and true.

The self-edge is cut slightly larger than the surface to which it will be adhered; then affixed to the wood with contact cement. With the workpiece clamped to the workbench, the excess laminate is trimmed off with the straight bit.

Next, the top is bonded (again with slight overhang all around) and trimmed with the straight cutter. Finally, all edges are dressed with the bevel cutter. Beveling requires only a slight pass since very little stock is removed.

Dovetail joints

One of the strongest joints in woodworking, the dovetail is widely used in commercial furniture-making. With the help of a dovetail template and a suitable template guide, your dovetail joints will soon rank with the best. No matter which brand of template and guide you buy, make certain you read and understand the manufacturer's instructions.

To make dovetail joints, first install the template guide in the router sub-base. (Note: Since the method of affixing guides varies from maker to maker, buy guides of the same make as your router.) Next, with the router installed in the sub-base (shoe), insert the dovetail bit so it extends exactly $^{19}/_{32}$ in. below the router base.

The base of the dovetail template is always affixed to a piece of wood (or the workbench). Use

VIEWED FROM the bottom the shoe of the router sits squarely on the wood surface with the bit cutting out a groove. The shoe should have enough solid surface to ride on so that it won't rock. Cutting grooves and dadoes such as this is the most common and simplest use for a router.

HOW TO CUT DECORATIVE EDGES THAT IMPROVE YOUR PROJECTS

PILOT BIT (here, a beading cutter) can be used around the edge of either a square or free-form workpiece.

TYPICAL EDGES shaped using a pilot-type bit: rounded-over (quarter round) at top and beading.

ROMAN OGEE illustrates how flutes do the cutting as the pilot at bottom rides against the work edge.

LIPPED DOOR is formed using rounding-over bit on the outside edges and ⅜-in. rabbet cutter on inside.

HOW TO HANDLE CIRCULAR WORK WITH NO CHANCE OF ERROR

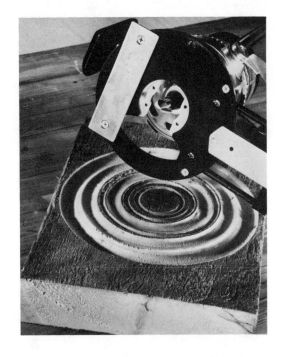

TRAMMEL POINT is affixed at the desired radius on guide bar secured in router shoe; straight bit does the cutting. The decorative plaque (right) was created with a core-box bit set at various depths for the concentric circles.

WORKING WITH PLASTIC LAMINATES

1. SELF-EDGE is applied to the top and trimmed with a straight carbide bit. Type shown is solid, one-piece.

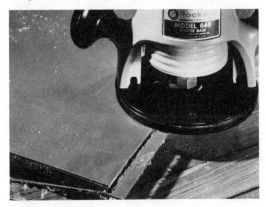

2. LAMINATE TOP is placed and trimmed, using the same cutter. See text for ways to prevent burns.

flathead screws in screwholes provided in the base. When clamped in position, the front (overhanging) apron of the base should butt against the front edge of the workbench or board fastened to the base.

With the template set up as instructed by the maker, always make a test dovetail joint first on scrap of the same material with which you will work. Make no mistake, dovetailing is precise work, so solve all problems—settings, cutter depth and the like—before pushing the router

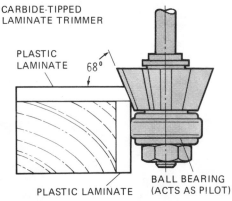

CARBIDE-TIPPED
LAMINATE TRIMMER

PLASTIC
LAMINATE   68°

PLASTIC LAMINATE

BALL BEARING
(ACTS AS PILOT)

3. EDGE is finish-dressed with bevel. Ball-bearing type bit is also fitted with a carbide tip.

DOVETAILING THE EASY WAY—WITH POWER

TO CUT DOVETAILS, you need a dovetail bit and template guide in router shoe and the dovetail template (below).

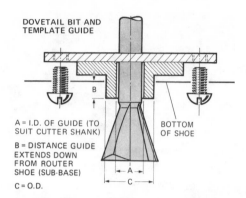

DOVETAIL BIT AND TEMPLATE GUIDE

A = I.D. OF GUIDE (TO SUIT CUTTER SHANK)
B = DISTANCE GUIDE EXTENDS DOWN FROM ROUTER SHOE (SUB-BASE)
C = O.D.

BOTTOM OF SHOE

TEMPLATE GUIDE must be securely fastened to the router shoe and the bit set at the precise cutting depth.

through your work. After obtaining a perfect cut on scrap, you can proceed on the work.

Since the boards are reversed after you make the cut, both boards are placed in the template with inside edges facing out and up. The top (horizontal) piece is first placed temporarily against the left-hand stop with its end extending about ½ in. beyond the main template base. Then the second piece is placed underneath the finger template and against the other left-hand stop. At the same time, move the first piece until it is flush with the second. When both pieces are perfectly lined up, tighten all template thumbscrews.

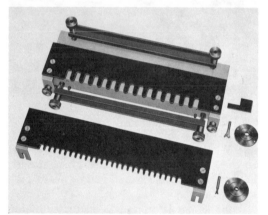

DOVETAIL TEMPLATE component parts: Notice that the main base is fastened to wood to provide clamping area.

WITH BOTH PIECES clamped in the template, router is moved left to right along complete edge (to prevent splintering). Second pass is also left to right, following fingers. The work is then test-fitted (right).

TEMPLATE ROUTING

TEMPLATE CUTTING is done using a template guide and pattern cut slightly under the finish-work size.

Freehand routing

A REAL CHALLENGE for a creative craftsman, freehand routing is done without guides or templates.

When making the dovetail cut, never move the router on or off the template with motor running; there's too high a risk of damaging the template with the cutter. And always make your first cut along the entire edge of the workpiece—without sliding in and out of the fingers—to prevent chipping the edge.

After moving the router from left to right for this first cut, shape the dovetails carefully, moving in and out of the fingers. Again, the router should be walked from left to right. After the cut is completed, turn off the router. When the cutter stops spinning, remove router from the work.

Remove the boards from the template and test the joint. If your test work on scrap was accurate, you should have a perfect joint. But if fit is loose, lower the bit slightly (perhaps 1/64 in.), replace boards in template and re-rout. (If tight, raise the bit by that distance.) Once the template and router are set to produce a perfect dovetail joint, any number of dovetails can be cut accurately. Rabbeted drawer fronts, as well as the joint, can be dovetailed, too; it is necessary to reset the template stops, and you should refer to the manual packed with your template

Template routing

Template guides are available in various sizes. The B dimension of the guide must be less than the thickness of the template you are using or the router will not sit flat on the template. The i.d. of the guide (A) should be slightly larger than the diameter of the router bit to assure clearance. Work being cut will vary in size, by the distance between the cutting edge of the bit and the o.d. of the guide (C). Be sure to allow for this offset when cutting your template (master pattern).

To make the cut, clamp the template to the piece to be routed. With a straight bit in the

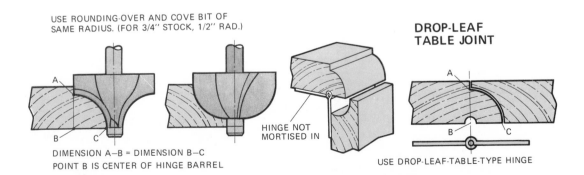

USE ROUNDING-OVER AND COVE BIT OF SAME RADIUS. (FOR 3/4" STOCK, 1/2" RAD.)

DIMENSION A—B = DIMENSION B—C
POINT B IS CENTER OF HINGE BARREL

HINGE NOT MORTISED IN

DROP-LEAF TABLE JOINT

USE DROP-LEAF-TABLE-TYPE HINGE

router, plunge the spinning cutter into the work until the router base is flat on the template. Then, follow the pattern, making certain that the template guide is *always in contact with the pattern*. Since there is no wear and tear, the template can be saved for future use.

Freehand routing

Once you've gained experience and confidence, you'll find the router an extremely efficient shaping and carving tool when used freehand. It can be used to turn out decorative items, lettered signs and the like in minimum time. Remember that the deeper the depth cut, the slower the rate of feed (there's more resistance to your movements).

You can rout out the design proper as illustrated in the photo or raise the design by routing out the background. Frequently, in freehand routing it is a must to affix a long board to the router base so that the router will straddle the routed-out sections in the work. Simply cut the board to desired length, drill two holes to suit the router shoe and countersink them for screws.

Drop-leaf table joint

A cove bit is used to make the concave cut on the table leaf; a rounding-over bit—of the same radius properly extended—makes the cut in the tabletop. Use a core-box bit for the barrel hinge mortise; its location must be precise. This is a tricky joint, so first test on scrap before routing the work.

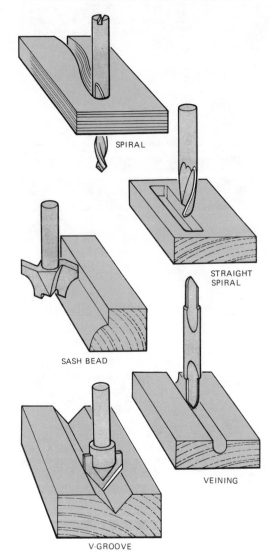

SPECIAL PURPOSE BITS FOR EXPERTS

SPIRAL

STRAIGHT SPIRAL

SASH BEAD

VEINING

V-GROOVE

Craftsman's secrets for using a router

■ THE ROUTER is a high-speed tool that performs similarly to the stationary shaper except that it is taken to the workpiece instead of the other way around. It can be used for certain other tasks such as trimming high-pressure plastic laminates, mortising for door hinges and making dovetails.

Routers come with speeds from 20,000 to 28,000 rpm. The reason for the high speed is that many shaped edges will not allow hand sanding; they must be smooth enough to finish as soon as they are made. Thus, if you buy a router with a speed of 25,000 rpm you'll get 50,000 blade passes a minute when you use a two-flute bit. That's impressive.

Make it your habit from the start to disconnect the tool from power whenever changing bits. Insert the desired bit into the collet until it bottoms, then back it out 1/16 to 1/8 in. This procedure is to protect the collet from breaking due to heat expansion.

Make absolutely certain that the collet is *fully tightened* before restoring power to your router. Failure to correctly install a bit and tighten the collet could result in a bit hurtling about the room like a piece of shrapnel.

Next, reassemble the motor into the base (on some models you just have to loosen a wingnut on the base). Slide the motor fully into the base and tighten the wingnut.

VERSATILE ROUTER is a must-own tool for serious woodworkers. Here, V-groove is routed using tacked-on straightedge. Strip against which router shoe rides must project past workpiece to prevent mishap.

GENERAL INFORMATION

TYPICAL home router consists of two basic parts: motor which holds bit, and base section for holding and guiding the working half of the tool.

TO CHANGE cutters, start by loosening device holding motor in base. Here, there's thumbnut and slotted screw.

QUICKEST way to change bits is to separate motor and base. Bit can be changed with unit intact, if preferred.

MANUFACTURER supplies wrenches for loosening split collet. Pressure is exerted in opposite directions.

INSERT the bit all the way, then withdraw about 1/16 in. for expansion.

WHEN SHANK is at the desired position, retighten collet with wrenches.

TO SET cutter depth, use a scaled ring supplied on many routers or simply check the bit with a ruler. Here, rabbet cutter is set to 3/8 in. depth.

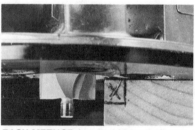

EASY METHOD is to hold installed cutter against marked workpiece. Waste is marked with X to prevent miscut.

FINISHED rabbeted edge is cut using bit set as shown in preceding photos. The cut is right on the mark.

Installing and removing a bit from a router varies slightly from one brand to another but, basically, the how-to procedure is quite similar. The router, in fact, grips a bit by its shank, somewhat like a drill grips a drill bit. The difference is that instead of three jaws closing around the shank, most routers have a split-nut collet which closes tightly as a second nut is tightened.

Read the instruction book packed with your tool for the correct how-to.

To use the micrometer ring on a router to set bit depth, follow these steps:

1. Place the router on a flat surface.

2. Loosen the wingnut and slide the motor down until the bit barely touches the surface.

3. Retighten the wingnut.

4. Rotate the depth adjustment ring until it hits the base. Now the bit is set for 0 in. depth of cut.

5. Note the position of the graduations on the depth-adjusting ring in relation to the index on the router base (usually a point, or arrow).

6. Rotate the ring in the appropriate direction to achieve the desired depth of cut. On some routers the depth is changed by 1/64 in. for every three graduation lines; thus the depth is changed 1/32 in. for every six graduation lines.

7. Loosen the wingnut and slide the motor as far into the base as the depth-adjusting ring permits. Retighten the wingnut and you can put the router to work.

Pro trick: Certain cutters are used more often than others in the type of woodworking most of

CUTTERS TO HAVE IN YOUR ACCESSORY BOX

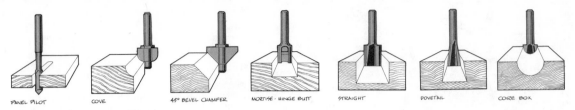

PANEL PILOT   COVE   45° BEVEL CHAMFER   MORTISE - HINGE BUTT   STRAIGHT   DOVETAIL   CORE BOX

THE V-GROOVE and bead bits which are presented on the preceding pages as well as those pictured above and on the opposite page are available in many sizes. Methods of using the bits are described in text.

GUIDING YOUR ROUTER

WITH THE ASSISTANCE of an edge guide, it's even possible to rout a circle.

ALL MAKERS produce edge guides for their routers.

PROJECTING GUIDE STRIP gets cutter into the workpiece without mishap. The work, in turn, is clamped to the workbench (clamp not visible).

us do. This includes the rabbet and straight (mortise) cutters. Make up a board with both of these cuts plowed to exactly ¼- and ⅜-in. depths—the usual depths for working with ¾-in.-thick boards. Each time you need to set a ⅜-in. rabbet cutter ⅜-in. deep, you don't have to fiddle with rulers; simply and quickly set the bit using the precut board.

There are five ways to guide a router:
1. With a pilot on the bit.
2. With an edge guide.
3. Freehand.
4. Against an edge.
5. With a templet guide.

Methods are listed in order, with the easiest first.

Guiding with a bit

Almost all decorative edging done with a router is with a bit that has a self-contained pilot. The pilot rides the edge of the material during the cut, so it is important that the edge be in perfect shape. For example, when putting an edge on a piece of plywood the pilot will enter any voids in the plywood, causing the decorative edging to indent, too.

When using a piloted bit make the cuts sequentially. Always start the router with the cutter standing away from the wood, then feed the spinning bit into the workpiece. Since the router bit spins in a clockwise direction, when viewed from above, an outside edge is always routed from left to right. Feed the tool in about ¼ in. or so from the left end of the board, push right for a

ROUNDING-OVER bit might well be first one you will purchase. This shape is available in at least four radii.

ROMAN OGEE is also a good bit to own; shape gives an attractive edge to plaques and the like. By using lower portion only, you create a small cove.

Router bits fall into two major classifications—one-piece bits and three-piece screw-type bits. All are of high-quality steel that has been heat-treated for hardness (so the cutting edges will be retained over fairly long periods of use).

If you plan on doing a lot of woodworking you should consider purchasing carbide-tipped bits on those shapes you'll use most often.

EDGE GUIDE on this router is installed into two holes in router base.

THUMBSCREWS are finger-tightened so that rods are secure, but movable. Next, router is turned over and guide set the desired distance from bit.

THUMBSCREWS are securely tightened; you might damage workpiece if edge guide should shift. To rout, lower spinning cutter into work.

If you buy your router in a kit form, which generally means it comes with a carrying case, the chances are the manufacturer will include a router-edge guide. If not, be sure to buy one.

The router (except when you do freehand routing) must be guided to create the professional-looking finishing touches you want. Thus, when you work with a straight (nonpiloted) bit you'll often need an edge guide.

The guide used to control the router is also handy for cutting along the edge of

a board. It is particularly useful for routing decorative grooves parallel to the edge of a board and for cutting grooves on long pieces of lumber. It is frequently used in mortise and dovetail work.

The edge-guide installation may vary from that shown. Here, the two rods are installed in holes provided on the base. They are held by tightening the machine screws already in the base. The guide is then installed on the rods and slid in or out until the correct distance from bit to guide is obtained. Thumbscrews are

then tightened.

Some craftsmen measure from bit center to edge guide, while others work with dimensions from bit edge to guide.

To start shaping, butt the guide against board edge, tilt-elevate the router to clear the cutter from wood and start the motor. Then lower the cutter into the workpiece.

The router will do far more than simply make decorative edges on boards. Try rigging a setup for cutting dovetail-shaped "tongue and grooves" on boards to be edge-joined.

---

couple of inches, then bring the tool all the way to the left and off the board. If you are routing just the one edge, don't allow the pilot to turn the board corner or you will edge-shape the end of the board as well. If necessary, you can tack a guide to the workpiece in order to prevent this. in order to prevent this.

Several rules:

• Always rout the edge grains first as shown in the drawing. You will learn that as the router bit exits an end grain on the far end it is not uncommon to have some splintering. If this is your last pass, it means that the finished adjacent edge may be splintered. But, done correctly, end grain first, the following pass—with the grain—will remove the splintered wood.

• A constant rate of feed is important for achieving a smooth cut. The point is to work your tool so that the router is working at its highest possible rpm. This will vary, depending upon the material being worked, depth of cut, sharpness of cutter and so on.

• As soon as the cut is completed, release the trigger to turn off the power to the router. Do not put the tool down until the cutter stops spinning.

Using an edge guide

An edge guide should probably be the first accessory that you buy for your router. As can be seen in the photos it is particularly useful for cutting blind mortises and the like, such as for the hidden-spline miter joint.

OTHER STUNTS YOU SHOULD KNOW

WHEN face-routing a board it is often impossible to use clamps. Instead, nail-fasten cleat along bottom for gripping in vise. Caution: Make certain nails are not in cutter's path.

YOU CAN CUT dovetails to join boards with assistance of an edge guide and two pieces of scrap which are clamped on to support the router shoe. In this instance, it is particularly important for you to locate the edge guide accurately.

MORTISE SHAPE in mating edge is cut using same technique, but cutter is set to leave center (tenon) intact.

MAKING AN EDGE CUT

CORRECT WAY to shape an edge using a cutter with pilot bearing: Start cut about ¼ in. from left end and push router into wood until bearing makes full contact with edge. Then move router right.

Since a router bit revolves clockwise as you look down on it from above, feed the router in a counterclockwise direction when shaping an outside edge. Con-

CORRECT sequence for edge shaping is shown at right. When this work is handled properly, the router cuts a neat edge, as shown above.

versely, if routing an inner edge—that is, a cutout—feed the router in a clockwise manner. The point is to feed the cutter to the work so the cutting edges can do

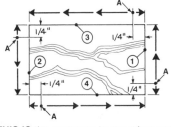

THIS IS the sequence to use when routing all four edges. Always shape end grains (1 and 2) first, then finish up by making with-the-grain passes (3 and 4). Points A are starting points for all four of the edges as shown in the diagram above.

their job. When shaping all four edges use the sequence shown. If you rout just one edge, be sure the pilot doesn't turn the corner.

Freehand work

Freehand routing is plain fun, even when you're just showing off. More often than not when routing freehand you will probably be making a sign or plaque.

There are two basic freehand techniques:

The letters or pattern can be cut directly into the wood.

You can rout out the background, leaving the letters raised from the surface.

To do freehand routing you must first put the pattern directly on the workpiece, using either a pencil or felt tip marker. Next, select the appropriate bit. Bits generally used for freehand work include the core box, straight (mortise type) for large areas and the veining bit for more delicate work.

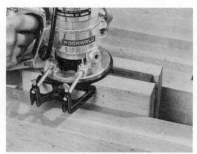

WHEN ROUTING freehand, work slowly and always push router so that cutter bites the wood as you go: Since the cutter spins clockwise—as you look down on it from above—push from left to right whenever possible. To make an S, for example, start at the bottom and work up.

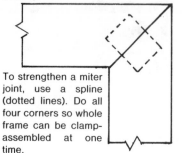

To strengthen a miter joint, use a spline (dotted lines). Do all four corners so whole frame can be clamp-assembled at one time.

YOU CAN strengthen otherwise weak miter joints by using splines. To create hidden splines, use your router. Clamp scrap stock on both sides of workpiece to keep router from wobbling, then grip setup in the bench vise. It's best to use edge guide to ensure accuracy.

The more you use a router, the greater your mastery of the tool will become. Once you are fully comfortable with it, you can try some of the more exotic router tasks such as cutting mortises for hidden splines and freehand routing.

Whenever you rout the narrow edge of a board you should increase the surface that the router shoe will ride on by clamping stock alongside as shown in the photos. The idea is to make certain that the router will not wobble as you

CUT SPLINE mortises in both work-pieces, then fashion the splines to suit openings they will fill. Here, in ⁵⁄₄-in. stock, ½-in. splines will be glued into mortise.

make your cut. If it does, damage to the workpiece is almost guaranteed.

Freehand routing is done with a core box or other straight bit. It requires full control by the operator; otherwise the stock will be wasted. The big trick is to work slowly—that is, push the router at a very slow feed rate.

No matter what new technique you try with a router it makes sense to perfect your skills first by practicing with scrap stock.

In general, you should not rout more than ¼ in. deep. The deeper the cut, the more difficult it will be to follow a pattern. Ordinarily, you should make the first depth setting equal to about 25 percent of the desired finish cut. The initial cut then acts as a guide for the final, full depth cutting.

Guiding against an edge

The fourth method for guiding a router is to keep the base against an edge of material. The edge can be straight, such as for plowing long grooves or dadoes, or it might be curved or scalloped to suit a custom task.

Clamp the board (or templet) securely to the top surface of the material being routed and guide the router in a counterclockwise rotation (left to right, as in edge shaping). Be sure to *keep the shoe in contact with the guide at all times.*

A typical application of such cutting would be the plowing of dadoes to receive let-in shelves, (on opposite vertical panels in a bookcase). Once the panels are laid out, they can be clamped or tacknailed together (side by side) so the grooves (dadoes) can be made across both boards at the same time.

Templet guides

Templet guides are accessories available for the router. Since these elevate the user into the world of advanced wood craftsmanship, some of the simpler do-it-yourself router models are not designed to accept templet guides.

The guides are locked in the router subbase using various means, depending upon the maker: Some are held with screws, others with locking nuts. In place, the guide's collar projects down from the shoe. The collar, in turn, rides a pattern edge, such a a dovetail templet or a templet for butt routing (routing the mortises for door hinges).

About bits

Over the long haul, you'll come out ahead if you purchase carbide-tipped bits to begin with. But this is true only for those who use a router fairly regularly.

Shaper from your router

■ IF YOU TURN a portable router upside down, you have, essentially, a wood-working shaper. To do it, the inverted router must be supported in such a way that it can function as a shaper with work guides, guards and the like. Di-mensions of the one shown here can be altered for your own router.

The router hangs suspended from the under-side of the cabinet top so that it can be removed for conventional routing operations by unscrewing four nuts. The hinged top tilts upward for convenience in changing cutters and making adjustments—although you can make cutter-height settings by reaching into the cabinet.

The cabinet top is hinged to the rear panel. Centered on the top is a $\frac{1}{16}$ x 8 x 8-in. aluminum plate that rests in a recess so the plate surface and adjacent wood are in the same plane. The hole at plate center is approximately $1\frac{1}{8}$ in. in diameter. In the wood top, concentric with this hole, is a 6-in.-dia. opening for the router base. Check your router's shoe diameter before cutting this circle.

You can form the $\frac{1}{16}$-in.-deep recess by routing out most of the area with a straight bit. Leave an "island" in the center until last so the router shoe is supported. Then, remove the island with a router bit in a drill press. Next, jigsaw the 6-in. opening. Fasten the plate in its recess with two countersunk wood screws near the opposite corners.

To determine the center of the $1\frac{1}{8}$-in. hole, insert a pointed cutter in the router and place the router base into its opening. The point where the bit touches the metal plate is the center for the hole. Use two 2-in. butt hinges to join top to back panel. Although the router's weight will hold the top down, rigidity is increased by installing a simple wooden latch at the corner near the front panel hinge.

The router-mounting arrangement is dictated by router-base construction. For the tool shown, two $\frac{1}{8}$ x $\frac{3}{4}$ x 7-in. aluminum strips, with $\frac{1}{16}$ x

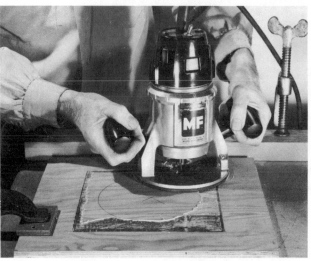

THE ROUTER cuts a recess in cabinet top to hold the plate against which router base is clamped.

BOTTOM OF the top panel shows the router clamped in place against the metal plate.

IN PARTIALLY assembled cabinet, the accessory drawer and vent openings for airflow are seen.

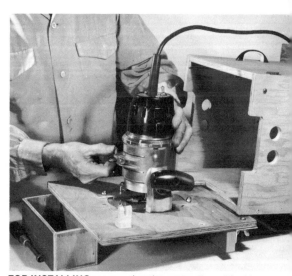

FOR INSTALLING or removing the router, the cabinet is flipped on its back and top panel swung open.

TO CHANGE cutters, the router is swung up and held by a dowel engaging sockets on the side panels.

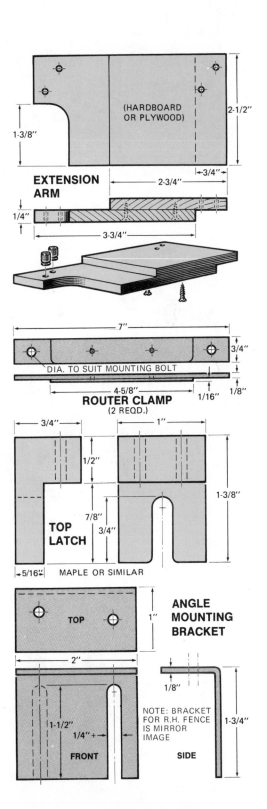

¾ x 4⅝-in. pads (to compensate for difference in router base and wood thickness) riveted to them, worked fine. Four 10–24 bolts extend through these strips, through countersunk holes in the metal top insert and plywood and are secured to the cabinet top with nuts and washers.

The cabinet and cabinet-top sizes are not critical. The dimensions given provide adequate space, although the power cord must be curved sideways in order to clear the bottom at the usual cutter depth settings.

Since a router motor "breathes" by drawing air in at cord-end and discharging it around the cutter, it's a must to provide airflow holes in the box. These consist of 1x4-in. notches at top edges of the sidepieces and back panel and multiple 1-in. holes in the back and front panels. (The two 1-in. holes at the top of each side are

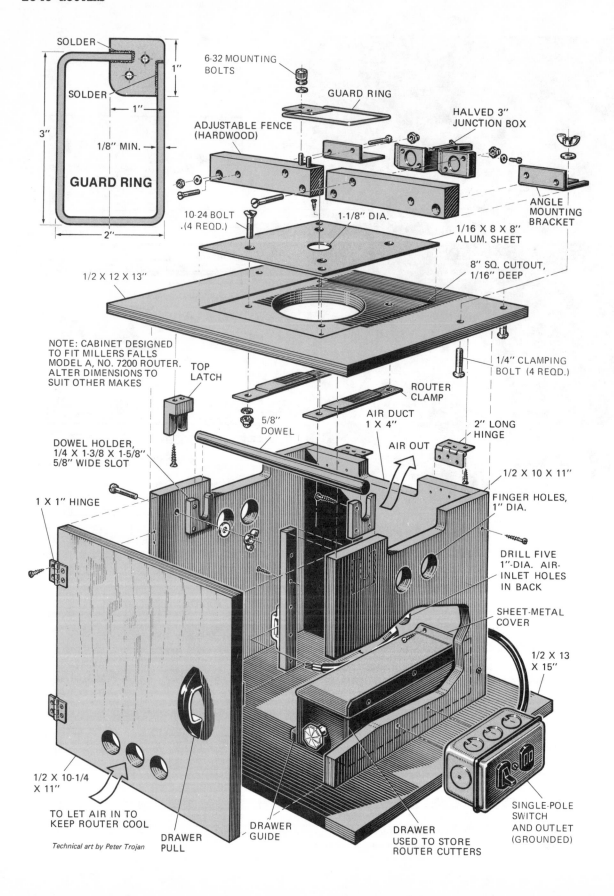

SOLDER

1''

SOLDER

3''

1''

1/8'' MIN.

GUARD RING

2''

6-32 MOUNTING BOLTS

GUARD RING

HALVED 3'' JUNCTION BOX

ADJUSTABLE FENCE (HARDWOOD)

ANGLE MOUNTING BRACKET

1/16 X 8 X 8'' ALUM. SHEET

10-24 BOLT .(4 REQD.)

1-1/8'' DIA.

8'' SQ. CUTOUT, 1/16'' DEEP

1/2 X 12 X 13''

NOTE: CABINET DESIGNED TO FIT MILLERS FALLS MODEL A, NO. 7200 ROUTER. ALTER DIMENSIONS TO SUIT OTHER MAKES

TOP LATCH

1/4'' CLAMPING BOLT (4 REQD.)

ROUTER CLAMP

5/8'' DOWEL

AIR DUCT 1 X 4''

2'' LONG HINGE

DOWEL HOLDER, 1/4 X 1-3/8 X 1-5/8'' 5/8'' WIDE SLOT

AIR OUT

1/2 X 10 X 11''

FINGER HOLES, 1'' DIA.

1 X 1'' HINGE

DRILL FIVE 1''-DIA. AIR-INLET HOLES IN BACK

SHEET-METAL COVER

1/2 X 13 X 15''

1/2 X 10-1/4 X 11''

TO LET AIR IN TO KEEP ROUTER COOL

Technical art by Peter Trojan

DRAWER PULL

DRAWER GUIDE

DRAWER USED TO STORE ROUTER CUTTERS

SINGLE-POLE SWITCH AND OUTLET (GROUNDED)

primarily finger holes for carrying.) If the intake air seems to carry excessive dust and chips, it's a good idea to install some fine-mesh screen over the inlets. Chips should not be permitted to build up in the box; if the router is to be used for long periods, periodically check the motor to avoid overheating. If necessary, leave the door open.

The hinged top can be raised to give better access to the router when you change cutters. The router is held in the tilted position by resting it on a piece of ⅝-in. dowel whose ends engage notched plywood pieces screwed to the inside surfaces of sidepieces.

The storage drawer is made of ¼-in. plywood and is located in one corner of the cabinet. To keep it in position, glue a guide strip along the bottom. A sheet-aluminum cover helps keep dirt out and the drawer in place. Inside, a wooden block drilled to receive cutter shanks holds stored cutters.

An adjustable fence guides straightedged work past the cutter. A piece of maple cut to the dimensions indicated was used here. An angle mounting bracket was then fastened to each end with bolts.

An adjustable bracket assembly made from a 3-in. electrical junction box (sawed diagonally in two) is bolted to the fence center. A little hammering and filing will let you fit the box halves squarely with the surfaces at a right angle and parallel where they contact the wood. Three 8–

INTERIOR VIEW shows the router in operating position. Original plastic shield was replaced by the ring type.

32 bolts hold the two halves together; holes in one of them are slotted so the guide fence can be adjusted for cut depth when jointing.

After bolting the junction-box bracket assembly to the wooden strip, saw a section slightly over 1 in. wide from the center of the strip to

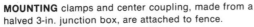

MOUNTING clamps and center coupling, made from a halved 3-in. junction box, are attached to fence.

REAR OF guide fence is in position for straight work. Notice the ring-type guard in foreground.

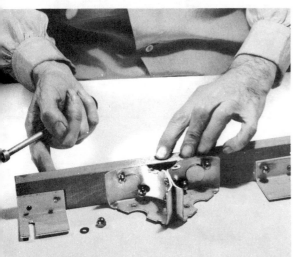

provide space for the cutter. Normally, the fence is used with surfaces of both halves in the same plane, but they can be offset as desired—by loosening the bolts holding the junction-box halves together. The fence assembly is centered with respect to the cutter, and holes for the ¼-in. clamping bolts are located near edges of the cabinet top. A second set of holes is drilled near the back edge of the top to provide an alternate fence position.

Make a guard ring to fit over the fence gap, which can also be used on an extension arm when nonstraight edges are being shaped. The loop, made from ⅛-in. rod, is soldered to a brass plate drilled for 6–32 mounting bolts. The extension arm, made from ¼-in. plywood, is stepped to bring it nearer the cutter and improve rigidity. Bolts holding the guard and extension arm should be in one half of the guide fence only so you can adjust the other half for depth of cut.

Because the router switch is not easily reached when the cabinet door is closed, you'll need an outside control. This consists of a single-pole switch and outlet (provided with ground connection) housed in a surface-mounting switch box screwed to the cabinet side. The router is plugged into the outlet.

A sizable assortment of cutters suitable for forming edge moldings, smoothing edges and other shaping chores is available. For use without a guide fence, as in cutting moldings along irregular edges, there are bits with pilots or shoulders to limit the cut. The setup illustrated had no tendency to "walk" because vibration is light. If desired, you can use C-clamps to anchor the cabinet on a table or bench.

Fingers should, of course, be kept away from cutters. Instead, various work hold-downs—such as springy steel strips—can be designed as needed, mounted on the fence and supplemented by push sticks to hold work against the cutter.

Your shaper cabinet can be finished conventionally. For the top, an easy finish is a sealer, such as thinned shellac, followed by two polish coats of floor wax. The rest of the cabinet can be varnished or painted.

TO SHAPE edges on straight work, a ring-type guard goes on the rear fence to protect fingers.

FOR CURVED work, guide fence is moved back. The ring guard is mounted on the extension.

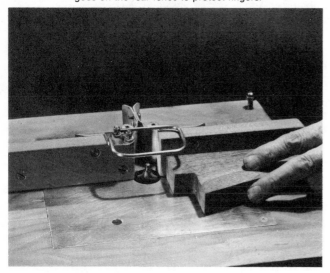

Sabre saw techniques

■ THE VERSATILE sabre saw can do practically any cutting job that can be done with a handsaw, jigsaw, bandsaw or even table and radial-arm saws—within limits of course. Circular-type saws can only cut in straight lines, while band and jigsaws can only handle materials as wide as the depth of their throat permits. In fact, certain jobs can only be done effectively with the sabre saw.

A wide variety of blades is available for cutting ferrous and nonferrous metal, wood, plastic, mineral and composition materials. For problem materials, such as ceramic tile, slate, cast stone and brick, a special blade edged with tungsten carbide grit is available. There is also a knife blade for cutting fibrous and rigid foam insulating materials, leather, rubber, cardboard, ceiling tile and wallboard. Most blades will fit all brands of saws.

For cutting woodwork, there are two basic kinds of blades: set tooth and hollow ground. Set blades have teeth which point alternately to each side. The set serves to cut a kerf wider than the back of the blade to allow it to pass through the cut without binding. Teeth of a hollow ground blade have no set—they're all in a line. However, the sides of the blade are tapered towards the back to provide clearance. Set teeth cut fast, but leave a rougher edge than the slower cutting hollow ground blade. The number of teeth per inch (TPI) is another factor—the more TPI, the slower and smoother the cut.

BLADES—number is teeth per inch. From left: 32 light gauge metal, 24 standard metal, 14 nonferrous metal, 20 wood scrolling, 7 wood roughing, 10 taper ground-wood, 12 reverse tooth-wood, flush cut, 3 wood rough, knife.

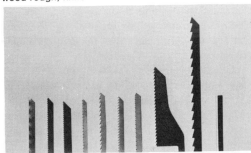

FLUSH-CUT blade aligns with shoe front, lets you cut to a vertical plane; especially good for floors.

A 6-IN. BLADE with 3 TPI (teeth per inch) is good for cutting through a 4x4. Use medium speed.

AT HIGH SPEED, A 32-TPI blade cuts sheet metal much quicker than could be done with snips.

LONG CURVES can best be cut with a flexible guidestrip (about ½ x ¾-in.) tacked in an offset position.

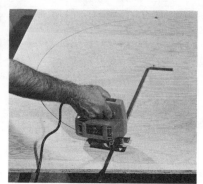

MAKE A pivot guide for cutting circles. This long one will reach beyond range of accessory guides.

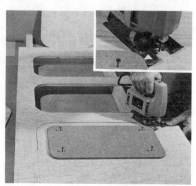

MASKING TAPE arrow on shoe (inset), aligned with blade teeth, keeps constant radius on curves.

When working with wood heavier than ¼-in., it is advisable to use a blade of ample width because narrow blades have a tendency to flex and drift off vertical. For any guided saw techniques shown, a set tooth blade is strongly recommended to get true cuts.

Cut with the wrong (back) side of workpiece facing up whenever possible. This is a good policy because blades usually cut on the upstroke, causing slight splintering—especially when sawing plywood. The exception is when using a reverse tooth blade—it cuts on the downstroke and makes right-side-up work possible.

Always clamp small pieces of work for safety and accuracy. The nature of the cutting action sets up considerable vibration.

It's wise to start your saw before touching the blade to the work. If the saw has variable speed, start the cut at low speed. It is often possible to start the cut by entering from the edge of the workpiece. When an inside or pocket cut is desired, the blade can be started in a predrilled

hole. For a rectangular-shaped pocket, drill a hole at each corner and then make straight cuts from hole to hole. If a straightedge (or pivot guide for circular cutouts) is to be used to obtain a precise outline, the size of the blade entry hole must be big enough to let the blade rest almost flush to the circumference of the hole.

Making a plunge cut is the alternative method for starting an interior cut and doesn't require a predrilled blade entry hole. Use a short, stout blade and tilt the saw forward so it rests on the front of the shoe with the blade not touching the work. Hold the saw firmly, turn to full speed and then slowly pivot the saw back to allow the blade to cut its way in. When the arc is completed and the base rests firmly on the work, advance saw to make the cut.

Intricate scrollwork calls for a narrow scrolling blade with 12 to 20 TPI and ³⁄₁₆ in. width. To support the work best, place it onto two lengths of 2x4 (set on edge) on the worktable. The 3½-in. standoff allows clearance for the blade. If the work has a delicate pattern, try to leave some uncut bridges in the waste area until the main parts have been cut.

Handy cross lap joints are advantageous for assembling large structural members and easy to make with a sabre saw. If the parts are to cross at other than right angles, determine the angle and tilt the saw shoe (or base) accordingly. Lock base into position and make double parallel cuts equal to the thickness of the stock, halfway through the planks. Chisel out the waste.

For smaller assemblies such as partitions for cabinets and built-ins, the same joint at right angles can be used. This should not be done freehand. Tack or clamp two straightedge strips of wood to the work, separated by the thickness of the work plus width of the shoe, less thickness of the blade. Run the saw along both sides of the guide strips halfway through the work and then remove the waste.

Making accurate rip or cross cuts requires an accessory guide for narrow widths and a straightedge guide for wider cuts. Clamp or tack-nail straightedge guide parallel to the line of cut (see photo).

Perfect circles are a cinch to cut with a sabre saw, but imperfect ones can easily result if you're not careful. T-shaped accessory rip guides are designed to also serve as circle guides. A nail driven through a hole in the crossbar support allows the saw to pivot in an arc. A blade entry hole tangent to the line of cut and in the waste area gets the blade started. Circle guides will work properly only if the front edge of the teeth and pivot point are equidistant from the support bar (see diagram).

The best way to cut *long sweeping curves* is with a sabre saw and a flexible wooden guide. Use a thin strip of wood, about ½ x ¾-in., bent to desired curve and tacked (on edge) to the workpiece. Position the guide so the saw will ride against the inside of the curve. Keep front and rear corners of the saw base in contact with the guide as you saw.

Template sawing economizes on both labor and lumber—and at the same time produces perfectly

TO MAKE GUIDE for oversize circle cut, use steel with same thickness and width as bar of accessory guide. Fold to form at one end and drill the pivot holes for various blade widths.

BASIC FREEHAND CUTS WITH VERSATILE SABRE SAW

CUTTING CIRCLES WITH PIVOT GUIDES

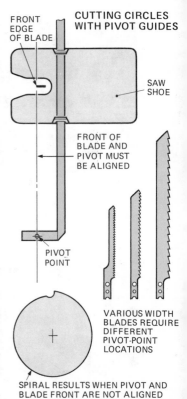

CUT ROUGH openings for soffit vents, louvers, stovepipes and more.

FOR PLUNGE CUT, use short, stout blade. Pivot blade into wood.

TO MINIMIZE vibration damage, hands and feet of figure are cut last.

FRONT EDGE OF BLADE

SAW SHOE

FRONT OF BLADE AND PIVOT MUST BE ALIGNED

PIVOT POINT

VARIOUS WIDTH BLADES REQUIRE DIFFERENT PIVOT-POINT LOCATIONS

SPIRAL RESULTS WHEN PIVOT AND BLADE FRONT ARE NOT ALIGNED

fitted flush doors or drawer fronts on plywood constructions such as bunk beds, cabinets and built-ins. Lay out the area to be cut by first measuring the distance between the shoe edge and the side of the blade. Double this figure and subtract it from the length and width of the desired opening.

Use these new dimensions to make the template from ¼-in. hardboard or plywood and round the corners to the desired radius. Next, center and tack the template over the opening area. Bore a blade entry hole equal to the thickness of the blade and centered on a straight segment of the line to be cut. Elongate the hole with a coping saw blade, just enough for the blade to be inserted. Place a masking tape arrow on the shoe's edge precisely opposite the blade teeth. Insert the saw blade and start the cut with the saw base pressed against the template edge. When you get to a corner curve, do not sharply pivot the saw. Instead, slowly advance it, keeping arrow point in contact with curved edge of the template.

Mortising jig is made by cutting an opening in a piece of hardboard or plywood. The width is determined by adding the saw base width to the width of the desired mortise and subtracting the thickness of the blade. The length of the jig opening is determined by adding the length of the mortise to the length of the shoe and subtracting the width of the blade. The rectangular jig can be made in two sections consisting of a U shape and a straight back piece. Bore a blade entry hole as wide as the slot near one end of the proposed mortise. Tack the jig into position so it will put the blade on one of the lines of cut. Insert the saw and make two forward cuts with saw base alternately pressed against each side of the jig. Make repeated cuts to clear out waste.

To square the end, slide the saw laterally against the jig's front. To cut out back of slot, reverse the blade so teeth point to the rear. Return saw to the jig and repeat cuts by pushing the saw backward.

CUTTING BEVELS—EVEN IN HEAVY STOCK

SHOE PLATE on most saws rotates between 45° and 90°.

ANGLED CROSSLAP joint is strong, easy to cut. Chisel away waste.

CONTROLLED CUTS WITH GUIDES AND TEMPLATES

TO MODIFY accessory rip guide, add wood strip for sure contact with work.

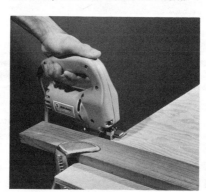

CLAMPED-ON straightedge guides should extend beyond both ends.

MORTISING TECHNIQUE WITH TEMPLATE

RECTANGULAR hardboard jig permits accurate mortising in table leg.

WITH BLADE reversed, saw is pushed backward to complete mortise.

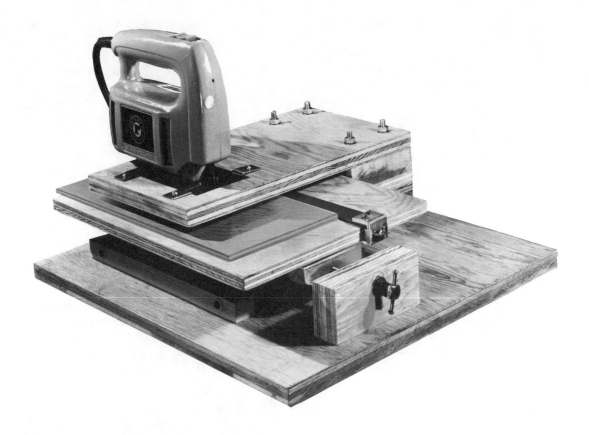

Table saw from your sabre saw

■ NUMEROUS SMALL sawing jobs often create handling problems that are as large as those you face when you're single-handedly maneuvering a 4x8 sheet of ¾-inch particleboard. From time to time, many woodworkers are challenged with the task of sabre-saw cutting a piece of board that's just too small to be clamped or to be held securely by hand. And for such small jobs as cutting thin strips from veneers and plywoods less than ½-inch thick a table saw is actually too big. One way to overcome such irritating challenges is with the use of the shop-built sabre-saw table shown below.

While this fixture was designed to accommo-

date a Model 68 Rockwell tool, you can alter the dimensions to suit any make and model of sabre saw (also known as a portable jigsaw).

Because a portable jigsaw cuts on its upstroke, the material being sawed must be held firmly against the saw platform. This is accomplished by a screw (bolt) that operates a parallel-bar arrangement, and through "cushioning" by a coil spring.

This ingenious table is built mostly of plywood. You'll find it easy to assemble if you follow the construction details shown.

First, attach the parallel-bar unit to the base panel with No. 8 fh screws running downward. Notice that the screwheads are flush with the bar surface. Secure the saw-platform supporting block with four ¼ x 5-in. carriage bolts (you may find that three bolts will be adequate). Wood screws installed from the bottom anchor the block in which the table-control screw operates.

The size of the saw cleanout opening is not critical; a 4x6-in. aperture will be adequate. The table is supported on furniture glide "feet," thus there is no need to countersink the screwheads into the bottom.

Glue together several 3⅞ x 7-in. pieces to form a platform supporting block that is about 3¹/₁₆ in. high. You'll find that a little testing will be in order to determine the height preferable for you. (When the table is at maximum height, it can be no closer than the thickness of the work-guide bar: on the stand shown, ⅛ in.)

Attach the four 10-in.-long bars to two pivot blocks with four wood screws. It's important to space these screws uniformly to assure accurate movement of the parallel bars. Fasten the work-support table to the parallel-bar unit with screws that run upward through the top bars, but not through the tabletop. The saw slot should be positioned after the stand has been assembled with the sabre saw in place.

The saw rests in a rectangular opening and is supported by a thin metal plate. Cut the plate slightly longer than the width of the plywood platform so that the front and rear edges can be bent slightly upward. Then you can anchor the saw in its recess with four L-shape clips secured with screws. The shorter ends of the clips will press downward on top of the saw base when the screws are tightened.

The table-height control was made from a ⁵/₁₆-18 x 4-in. bolt, with a rod crosswise through the head for easier turning without a wrench. The coil spring between the head and the block enables the table to "give" slightly and serves as

HOLES ARE BORED simultaneously through the saw platform and through the supporting block. The platform is secured temporarily with two nails.

BY REMOVING two pivot screws from the parallel-bar unit, the upper bars can be easily swung up for installation or removal of the table.

COMPONENT PARTS, parallel-bar unit, saw-platform-supporting block and adjusting-screw block are all firmly attached to the baseboard of ¾-in. plywood.

WORK GUIDE BAR is adjustable across the table and is locked in position with a special wingbolt which presses against front edge of the table when tightened.

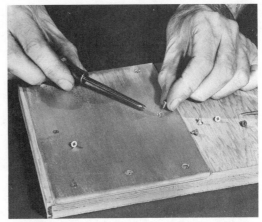

SHEET-ALUMINUM plate that supports the sabre saw is fastened to the bottom of the saw platform with eight tiny fh screws turned into countersunk holes.

SABRE-SAW BASE is anchored to the platform with four L-shaped metal clips spaced along the sides of the rectangular recess. Clips are attached with rh screws.

HERE'S HOW work is fed into the saw by passing it under saw-supporting platform and along the guide bar. Saw handles work to ½ in. thick and 6 in. wide.

WEAR SAFETY GOGGLES

an aid in preventing binding. A dab of oil or grease will lubricate the bolt in the threaded hole of the maple block. By turning the bolt in or out, you can raise or lower the table. The bolt moves up or down with the table and automatically adjusts itself in the slot of the block that's fixed to the base.

To use the stand, push material past the saw blade much the same as on a conventional table saw. Overhang of the saw platform and the table helps to shield the blade, while pusher sticks are used to move the work past the blade and out the rear of the opening between table and saw platform. The work-guide bar must be clamped securely enough not to yield under pressure applied to workpiece.

BASE

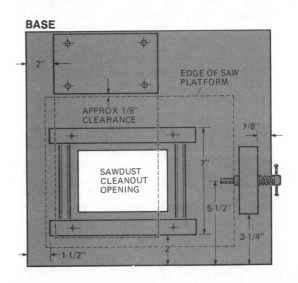

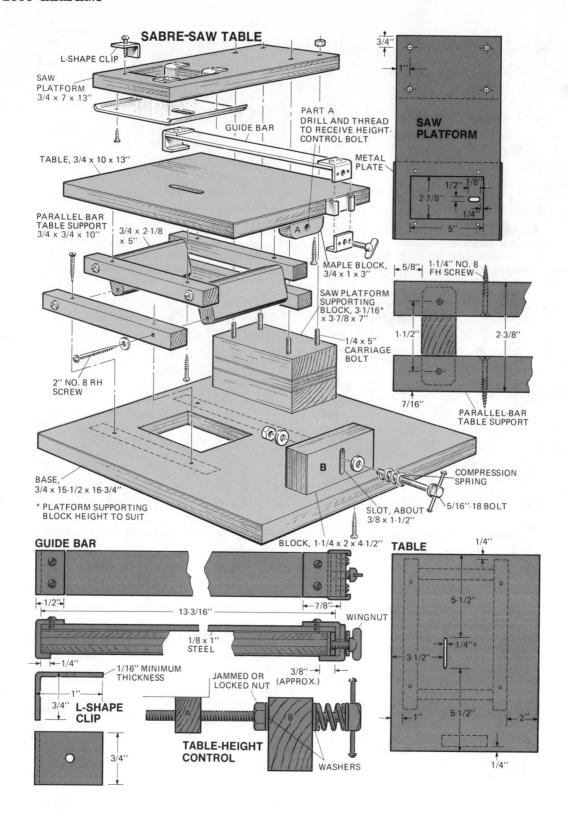

SABRE-SAW TABLE

L-SHAPE CLIP

SAW PLATFORM 3/4 x 7 x 13''

GUIDE BAR

PART A DRILL AND THREAD TO RECEIVE HEIGHT-CONTROL BOLT

METAL PLATE

TABLE, 3/4 x 10 x 13''

PARALLEL-BAR TABLE SUPPORT 3/4 x 3/4 x 10''

3/4 x 2-1/8 x 5''

MAPLE BLOCK, 3/4 x 1 x 3''

SAW PLATFORM SUPPORTING BLOCK, 3-1/16* x 3-7/8 x 7''

1/4 x 5'' CARRIAGE BOLT

2'' NO. 8 RH SCREW

BASE, 3/4 x 15-1/2 x 16-3/4''

* PLATFORM SUPPORTING BLOCK HEIGHT TO SUIT

BLOCK, 1-1/4 x 2 x 4-1/2''

SLOT, ABOUT 3/8 x 1-1/2''

COMPRESSION SPRING

5/16''-18 BOLT

SAW PLATFORM

3/4''
1''
1/2'' 7/8''
2-7/8''
1/4''
5''

5/8''

1-1/4'' NO. 8 FH SCREW

1-1/2''

2-3/8''

7/16''

PARALLEL-BAR TABLE SUPPORT

GUIDE BAR

1/2''
13-3/16''
7/8''

1/8 x 1'' STEEL

WINGNUT

1/4''

1/16'' MINIMUM THICKNESS

1''
3/4''

L-SHAPE CLIP

3/4''

JAMMED OR LOCKED NUT

A

3/8'' (APPROX.)

B

TABLE-HEIGHT CONTROL

WASHERS

TABLE

1/4''

5-1/2''

3-1/2''

1/4''+

1''

5-1/2''

2''

1/4''

INDEX · VOLUME 20

A

Adjustable fence for radial-arm saw, 2452

B

Bathroom scale: built-in, 2484
Bay window shutters, 2481
Bearing wall removal, 2505
Bed: fold-down, 2487
Bedroom remodeling, 2485
Bench
  entryway, 2482
  radial-arm saw, 2453
Bevel cuts with sabre saw, 2554
Bifold door track, concealing, 2482
Bits for routers, 2528
Blade types for sabre saws, 2551
Buffet cabinet, built-in, 2486

C

Cabinets
  buffet, built-in, 2486
  router, 2545
Campers
  improvements, 2471
  RV fit-out for camping, 2461
  vacation home with an RV, 2464
  winterizing, 2467
Circle cutting with sabre saws, 2553
Compartments: installing in RV, 2461
Compound miter cuts with radial-arm saw, 2438
Construction: header, 2507
Cottage: built around an RV, 2464
Craftman's router-use secrets, 2539
Crosscuts with radial-arm saws, 2437

D

Dadoes
  radial-arm saw cutting, 2447
  router cutting, 2531
Damaged roof repair, 2513
Decorative edging with a router, 2537
Disc sander: with radial-arm saw, 2438
Divider wall, 2520
Doors: sliding doors you can add, 2501
Dovetail joints: router cutting, 2533
Drop-leaf table joint with a router, 2537
Drum sander: with radial-arm saw, 2438

E

Edge cuts with a router, 2543

E

Electrical wiring: wall lighting, 2526
Entry wall, 2520
Entryway
  bench, 2482
  grille, 2483
Extension tables for radial-arm saw, 2447, 2456

F

Fences
  molding for radial-arm saw, 2452
  radial-saw bench extensions, 2453
Floors; remodeling, 2479
Fold-down bed, 2487
Freehand routing, 2538, 2543
Freestanding wall
  construction, 2523
  lighting, 2526

G

Garage bumper step, 2481
Grille for an entryway, 2483
Grooves: router cutting, 2531

H

Handrail to enhance your home, 2458
Heating recreational vehicles, 2472
Holding tank: recreational vehicles, 2471
Home remodeling
  adding stairs, 2500
  dramatic changes, 2496
  facelifting, 2492
  kitchens, 2490, 2498
  relocating stairs, 2494
  retaining walls, 2495
  techniques and tips, 2479

I

Improve your recreational vehicle, 2471

J

Jacks to level radial-saw table, 2457

K

Kitchen remodeling, 2490, 2498

M

Magazine rack: built-in, 2484
Miter cuts with radial-arm saw, 2438
Molding head fence for radial-arm saw, 2452
Molding head for radial-arm saw, 2440
Mortise cuts with sabre saw, 2554

N

Newel posts: railing construction, 2459

P

Painting: remodeling projects, 2479
Plastic laminates: router tips, 2537
Plunge cuts with sabre saw, 2553
Push stick with radial-arm saw, 2437

R

Rabbet: router cutting, 2531
Radial-arm saws
  accessory storage, 2443
  bench, 2453
  cabinet, 2443
  molding head fence, 2452
  operation, 2436
  safety tips, 2436
  table, 2447
  table extensions, 2456
  table jacks, 2457
Railings
  handrail, 2458
  mounting, 2458, 2459
  wrought-iron, 2459
Recreational vehicles
  camping fit-out, 2461
  improvements, 2471
  storing, 2467
  tent trailer, 2475
  vacation home, 2464
  winterize your camper, 2467
Red cedar shingles, 2515
Remodeling
  adding stairs, 2497
  bathroom scale built-in, 2484
  bay window shutters, 2481
  bedroom remodeling, 2485
  bifold door track, 2482
  buffet cabinet, built-in, 2486
  entryway bench, 2482
  entryway grille, 2483
  facelifting, 2492
  fold-down bed, 2487
  garage bumper step, 2481
  home, 2479, 2489, 2492, 2496
  kitchen, 2490, 2498
  magazine rack, built-in, 2484
  products available, 2480
  removing walls, 2479
  retaining walls, 2495
  roof line changes, 2497
  sliding doors, 2501
  stairs addition, 2497
  stairs relocation, 2494, 2497
  wall removal, 2505
  window casing: decorative, 2482
  window treatments, 2481
  windows, 2501
Rip cuts with radial-arm saw, 2437
Roman ogee cuts with router, 2542
Roofs
  changing lines in remodeling, 2497
  damaged, 2510, 2513
  estimating shingle squares, 2519
  repairing, 2510, 2513
  ridge treatment, 2512
  roofing yourself, 2509

shakes, 2515
sheathing, 2513
shingles, 2509, 2515
valley treatment, 2511
wood shakes and shingles, 2515
Room dividers
entry wall, 2521
freestanding wall, 2523
lighting a freestanding wall, 2526
see-through divider, 2520
storage wall, 2521
Rounding over edges with router, 2539
Routers
bits and accessories, 2528
cabinet, 2545
circular work, 2537
cutter installation, 2530
cutter types, 2541
decorative edging, 2537
dovetail joints, 2533
drop-leaf table joint, 2537
edge cut, 2543
freehand routing, 2538, 2543
groove and dado cutting, 2531
plastic laminates, 2532
rabbet cutting, 2531
Roman ogee cut, 2542
rounding over, 2542
safety, 2527
shaper, 2545
techniques, 2527

template routing, 2537, 2544
tips for using, 2527, 2539

_____ S _____

Sabre saws
bench, 2555
blades, 2551
circle cutting, 2553
plunge cut, 2551
table saw bench, 2555
techniques, 2552
Sanding with radial-arm saw, 2438
Sanitary system: recreational vehicles, 2474
Shakes: roofing, 2515
Shaper from your router, 2545
Shingles
installing, 2509, 2515
patching, 2513
shakes, 2515
wood, 2515
Squares: roof shingle measurement, 2519
Storage
bench for radial-arm saw, 2453
wall, 2521

_____ T _____

Table: radial-arm saw
construction, 2447
extensions, 2456
leveling jacks, 2457

Table saw from your sabre saw, 2555
Template routing, 2537, 2544
Tent trailer you can build, 2475
Tires: recreational vehicles, 2471
Trailers: tent, 2475

_____ V _____

Vacation home from your RV, 2464

_____ W _____

Walls
bedroom divider, 2523
dividers, 2520
entry, 2521
freestanding, 2523
lighting, 2526
removing for remodeling, 2480
see-through divider, 2520
storage, 2521
surface remodeling, 2479
Water tanks: recreational vehicles, 2471
Window
casing, decorative, 2482
treatments in remodeling, 2481
windows you can add, 2501
Winterize your camper, 2467
Wood shingles: roofing, 2515
Wrought-iron railing installation, 2459

CUSTOMARY TO METRIC (CONVERSION) Conversion factors can be carried so far they become impractical. In cases below where an entry is exact it is followed by an asterisk (*). Where considerable rounding off has taken place, the entry is followed by a + or a − sign.

Linear Measure

inches	millimeters
1/16	1.5875*
1/8	3.2
3/16	4.8
1/4	6.35*
5/16	7.9
3/8	9.5
7/16	11.1
1/2	12.7*
9/16	14.3
5/8	15.9
11/16	17.5
3/4	19.05*
13/16	20.6
7/8	22.2
15/16	23.8
1	25.4*

inches	centimeters
1	2.54*
2	5.1
3	7.6
4	10.2
5	12.7*
6	15.2
7	17.8
8	20.3
9	22.9
10	25.4*
11	27.9
12	30.5

feet	centimeters	meters
1	30.48*	.3048*
2	61	.61
3	91	.91
4	122	1.22
5	152	1.52
6	183	1.83
7	213	2.13
8	244	2.44
9	274	2.74
10	305	3.05
50	1524*	15.24*
100	3048*	30.48*

1 yard = .9144* meters
1 rod = 5.0292* meters
1 mile = 1.6 kilometers
1 nautical mile = 1.852* kilometers

Weights

ounces	grams
1	28.3
2	56.7
3	85
4	113
5	142
6	170
7	198
8	227
9	255
10	283
11	312
12	340
13	369
14	397
15	425
16	454

Formula (exact):
ounces × 28.349 523 125* = grams

pounds	kilograms
1	.45
2	.9
3	1.4
4	1.8
5	2.3
6	2.7
7	3.2
8	3.6
9	4.1
10	4.5

1 short ton (2000 lbs) = 907 kilograms (kg)
Formula (exact):
pounds × .453 592 37* = kilograms

Fluid Measure

(Milliliters [ml] and cubic centimeters [cc] are equivalent, but it is customary to use milliliters for liquids.)

1 cu in	= 16.39 ml
1 fl oz	= 29.6 ml
1 cup	= 237 ml
1 pint	= 473 ml
1 quart	= 946 ml
	= .946 liters
1 gallon	= 3785 ml
	= 3.785 liters

Formula (exact):
fluid ounces × 29.573 529 562 5* = milliliters

Volume

1 cu in	= 16.39 cubic centimeters (cc)
1 cu ft	= 28 316.7 cc
1 bushel	= 35 239.1 cc
1 peck	= 8 809.8 cc

Area

1 sq in	= 6.45 sq cm
1 sq ft	= 929 sq cm
	= .093 sq meters
1 sq yd	= .84 sq meters
1 acre	= 4 046.9 sq meters
	= .404 7 hectares
1 sq mile	= 2 589 988 sq meters
	= 259 hectares
	= 2.589 9 sq kilometers

Miscellaneous

1 British thermal unit (Btu) (mean) = 1 055.9 joules
1 horsepower = 745.7 watts
= .75 kilowatts
caliber (diameter of a firearm's bore in hundredths of an inch) = .254 millimeters (mm)

1 atmosphere pressure = 101 325* pascals (newtons per sq meter)
1 pound per square inch (psi) = 6 895 pascals
1 pound per square foot = 47.9 pascals
1 knot = 1.85 kilometers per hour
1 mile per hour = 1.6093 kilometers per hour